Chemistry revision? CGP has the solution...

No doubt about it, GCSE Chemistry is a tough subject. Luckily, this CGP book
is crammed full of info, from facts and theory to practical skills — and what's more,
there are practice questions on each page to help you sharpen up your exam skills.

CGP — still the best! ☺

Our sole aim here at CGP is to produce the highest quality books —
carefully written, immaculately presented and dangerously close to being funny.

Then we work our socks off to get them out to you
— at the cheapest possible prices.

Contents

Published by CGP

From original material by Richard Parsons

Editors: Katie Braid, Emily Howe, Robin Flello, Ciara McGlade and Hayley Thompson.
Contributors: Michael Bossart, Paddy Gannon and Mike Thompson.

Page 99 contains public sector information licensed under the Open Government Licence v3.0. http://www.nationalarchives.gov.uk/doc/open-government-licence/version/3/

With thanks to Sophie Scott and Jamie Sinclair for the proofreading.

With thanks to Ana Pungartnik for the copyright research.

Printed by Elanders Ltd, Newcastle upon Tyne.
Clipart from Corel®

The Scientific Method

This section <u>isn't</u> about how to 'do' science — but it does show you the way <u>most scientists</u> work.

Scientists Come Up With Hypotheses — Then Test Them

1) Scientists try to <u>explain</u> things. They start by <u>observing</u> something they don't understand.

2) They then come up with a <u>hypothesis</u> — a possible <u>explanation</u> for what they've observed.

3) The next step is to <u>test</u> whether the hypothesis might be <u>right or not</u>. This involves making a <u>prediction</u> based on the hypothesis and testing it by <u>gathering evidence</u> (i.e. <u>data</u>) from <u>investigations</u>. If <u>evidence</u> from <u>experiments</u> backs up a prediction, you're a step closer to figuring out if the hypothesis is true.

About 100 years ago, scientists hypothesised that atoms looked like this.

Several Scientists Will Test a Hypothesis

1) Normally, scientists <u>share</u> their <u>findings</u> in <u>peer-reviewed journals</u>, or at <u>conferences</u>.

2) <u>Peer-review</u> is where <u>other scientists</u> check results and scientific explanations to make sure they're 'scientific' (e.g. that experiments have been done in a sensible way) <u>before</u> they're published. It helps to <u>detect false claims</u>, but it doesn't mean that findings are <u>correct</u> — just that they're not wrong in any <u>obvious</u> way.

3) Once other scientists have found out about a hypothesis, they'll start basing their <u>own predictions</u> on it and carry out their <u>own experiments</u>. They'll also try to <u>reproduce</u> the original experiments to <u>check the results</u> — and if all the experiments in the world <u>back up</u> the <u>hypothesis</u>, then scientists start to think the hypothesis is <u>true</u>.

4) However, if a scientist does an experiment that <u>doesn't fit</u> with the hypothesis (and other scientists can reproduce the results) then the hypothesis may need to be <u>modified</u> or <u>scrapped</u> altogether.

After more evidence was gathered, scientists changed their hypothesis to this.

If All the Evidence Supports a Hypothesis, It's Accepted — For Now

1) <u>Accepted hypotheses</u> are often referred to as <u>theories</u>. Our <u>currently</u> <u>accepted</u> theories are the ones that have survived this 'trial by evidence' — they've been <u>tested many times</u> over the years and <u>survived</u>.

2) However, theories <u>never</u> become totally indisputable <u>fact</u>. If <u>new evidence</u> comes along that <u>can't be explained</u> using the existing theory, then the hypothesising and testing is likely to <u>start all over again</u>.

Now we think it's more like this.

Theories Can Involve Different Types of Models

1) A <u>representational model</u> is a <u>simplified description</u> or <u>picture</u> of what's going on in real life. Like all models, it can be used to <u>explain observations</u> and <u>make predictions</u>. E.g. the <u>Bohr model</u> of an atom is a simplified way of showing the arrangement of electrons in an atom (see p.19). It can be used to explain trends down groups in the periodic table.

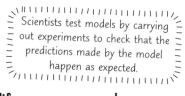

Scientists test models by carrying out experiments to check that the predictions made by the model happen as expected.

2) <u>Computational models</u> use computers to make <u>simulations</u> of complex real-life processes, such as climate change. They're used when there are a <u>lot</u> of different <u>variables</u> (factors that change) to consider, and because you can easily <u>change their design</u> to take into account <u>new data</u>.

3) All models have <u>limitations</u> on what they can <u>explain</u> or <u>predict</u>. E.g. <u>ball and stick models</u> (a type of spatial model) can be used to show how ions are arranged in an ionic compound. One of their limitations is that they <u>don't show</u> the <u>relative sizes</u> of the ions (see p.30).

I'm off to the zoo to test my hippo-thesis...

The scientific method has developed over time, and many people have helped to develop it. From Aristotle to modern day scientists, lots of people have contributed. And many more are likely to contribute in the future.

Communication & Issues Created by Science

Scientific developments can be great, but they can sometimes <u>raise more questions</u> than they answer...

It's Important to Communicate Scientific Discoveries to the General Public

Some scientific discoveries show that people should <u>change their habits</u>, or they might provide ideas that could be <u>developed</u> into new <u>technology</u>. So scientists need to <u>tell the world</u> about their discoveries.

Technologies are being developed that make use of <u>fullerenes</u> (see p.34). These include <u>drug delivery systems</u> for use in medicine. Information about these systems needs to be communicated to <u>doctors</u> so they can <u>use</u> them, and to <u>patients</u>, so they can make <u>informed decisions</u> about their <u>treatment</u>.

Scientific Evidence can be Presented in a Biased Way

1) Reports about scientific discoveries in the <u>media</u> (e.g. newspapers or television) <u>aren't</u> peer-reviewed.

2) This means that, even though news stories are often <u>based</u> on data that has been peer-reviewed, the data might be <u>presented</u> in a way that is <u>over-simplified</u> or <u>inaccurate</u>, making it open to <u>misinterpretation</u>.

3) People who want to make a point can sometimes <u>present data</u> in a <u>biased way</u>. (Sometimes <u>without knowing</u> they're doing it.) For example, a scientist might overemphasise a relationship in the data, or a newspaper article might describe details of data <u>supporting</u> an idea without giving any evidence <u>against</u> it.

Scientific Developments are Great, but they can Raise Issues

Scientific <u>knowledge is increased</u> by doing experiments. And this knowledge leads to <u>scientific developments</u>, e.g. new technologies or new advice. These developments can create <u>issues</u> though. For example:

<u>Economic issues:</u> Society <u>can't</u> always <u>afford</u> to do things scientists recommend (e.g. investing in alternative energy sources) without <u>cutting back elsewhere</u>.

<u>Personal issues:</u> Some decisions will affect <u>individuals</u>. For example, someone might support <u>alternative energy</u>, but object if a <u>wind farm</u> is built next to their house.

<u>Social issues:</u> Decisions based on scientific evidence affect <u>people</u> — e.g. should fossil fuels be taxed more highly? <u>Would the effect on people's lifestyles be acceptable...</u>

<u>Environmental issues:</u> <u>Human activity</u> often affects the <u>natural environment</u>. For example, building a <u>dam</u> to produce electricity will change the <u>local habitat</u> so some species might be displaced. But it will also reduce our need for <u>fossil fuels</u>, so will help to reduce <u>climate change</u>.

Science Can't Answer Every Question — Especially Ethical Ones

1) We don't <u>understand everything</u>. We're always finding out <u>more</u>, but we'll never know <u>all</u> the answers.

2) In order to answer scientific questions, scientists need <u>data</u> to provide <u>evidence</u> for their hypotheses.

3) Some questions can't be answered <u>yet</u> because the data <u>can't</u> currently be <u>collected</u>, or because there's <u>not enough</u> data to <u>support</u> a theory.

4) <u>Eventually</u>, as we get <u>more evidence</u>, we'll answer some of the questions that <u>currently</u> can't be answered, e.g. what the impact of global warming on sea levels will be. But there will always be the "<u>Should we be doing this at all?</u>"-type questions that experiments <u>can't</u> help us to answer...

Think about <u>new drugs which can be taken to boost your 'brain power'</u>.

- Some people think they're <u>good</u> as they could improve concentration or memory. New drugs could let people think in ways beyond the powers of normal brains.

- Other people say they're <u>bad</u> — they could give you an <u>unfair advantage</u> in exams. And people might be <u>pressured</u> into taking them so that they could work more <u>effectively</u>, and for <u>longer hours</u>.

THE GAZETTE
BRAIN-BOOSTING DRUGS MAKE A MOCKERY OF EXAMS

THE POST
GENIUS PILLS TO BECOME THE NEW COFFEE

Tea to milk or milk to tea? — Totally unanswerable by science...

Science can't tell you whether or not you should do something. That's for you and society to decide. But there are tons of questions science might be able to answer, like where life came from and where my superhero socks are.

Risk

By reading this page you are agreeing to the risk of a paper cut or severe drowsiness...

Nothing is Completely Risk-Free

1) A hazard is something that could potentially cause harm.

2) All hazards have a risk attached to them — this is the chance that the hazard will cause harm.

3) The risks of some things seem pretty obvious, or we've known about them for a while, like the risk of causing acid rain by polluting the atmosphere, or of having a car accident when you're travelling in a car.

4) New technology arising from scientific advances can bring new risks, e.g. scientists are unsure whether nanoparticles that are being used in cosmetics and suncream might be harming the cells in our bodies. These risks need to be considered alongside the benefits of the technology, e.g. improved sun protection.

5) You can estimate the size of a risk based on how many times something happens in a big sample (e.g. 100 000 people) over a given period (e.g. a year). For example, you could assess the risk of a driver crashing by recording how many people in a group of 100 000 drivers crashed their cars over a year.

6) To make decisions about activities that involve hazards, we need to take into account the chance of the hazard causing harm, and how serious the consequences would be if it did. If an activity involves a hazard that's very likely to cause harm, with serious consequences if it does, it's considered high risk.

People Make Their Own Decisions About Risk

1) Not all risks have the same consequences, e.g. if you chop veg with a sharp knife you risk cutting your finger, but if you go scuba-diving you risk death. You're much more likely to cut your finger during half an hour of chopping than to die during half an hour of scuba-diving. But most people are happier to accept a higher probability of an accident if the consequences are short-lived and fairly minor.

2) People tend to be more willing to accept a risk if they choose to do something (e.g. go scuba diving), compared to having the risk imposed on them (e.g. having a nuclear power station built next door).

3) People's perception of risk (how risky they think something is) isn't always accurate. They tend to view familiar activities as low-risk and unfamiliar activities as high-risk — even if that's not the case. For example, cycling on roads is often high-risk, but many people are happy to do it because it's a familiar activity. Air travel is actually pretty safe, but a lot of people perceive it as high-risk.

4) People may over-estimate the risk of things with long-term or invisible effects, e.g. ionising radiation.

Investigations Can be Hazardous

1) Hazards from science experiments might include:

- Microorganisms, e.g. some bacteria can make you ill.
- Chemicals, e.g. sulfuric acid can burn your skin and alcohols catch fire easily.
- Fire, e.g. an unattended Bunsen burner is a fire hazard.
- Electricity, e.g. faulty electrical equipment could give you a shock.

Hmm... Where did my bacteria sample go?

2) Part of planning an investigation is making sure that it's safe.

3) You should always make sure that you identify all the hazards that you might encounter. Then you should think of ways of reducing the risks from the hazards you've identified. For example:

- If you're working with sulfuric acid, always wear gloves and safety goggles. This will reduce the risk of the acid coming into contact with your skin and eyes.
- If you're using a Bunsen burner, stand it on a heat proof mat. This will reduce the risk of starting a fire.

You can find out about potential hazards by looking in textbooks, doing some Internet research, or asking your teacher.

Not revising — an unacceptable exam hazard...

The world's a dangerous place, but if you can recognise hazards, decide how to reduce their risks, and be happy to accept some risks, you can still have fun. Just maybe don't go skydiving with a great white shark on Friday 13th.

Designing Investigations

Dig out your lab coat and dust down your badly-scratched safety goggles... it's investigation time.

Investigations Produce Evidence to Support or Disprove a Hypothesis

1) Scientists observe things and come up with hypotheses to explain them (see p.2).
You need to be able to do the same. For example:

> Observation: People have big feet and spots. Hypothesis: Having big feet causes spots.

2) To determine whether or not a hypothesis is right, you need to do an investigation to gather evidence. To do this, you need to use your hypothesis to make a prediction — something you think will happen that you can test. E.g. people who have bigger feet will have more spots.

3) Investigations are used to see if there are patterns or relationships between two variables, e.g. to see if there's a pattern or relationship between the variables 'number of spots' and 'size of feet'.

Evidence Needs to be Repeatable, Reproducible and Valid

1) Repeatable means that if the same person does an experiment again using the same methods and equipment, they'll get similar results.

2) Reproducible means that if someone else does the experiment, or a different method or piece of equipment is used, the results will still be similar.

Investigations include experiments and studies.

3) If data is repeatable and reproducible, it's reliable and scientists are more likely to have confidence in it.

4) Valid results are both repeatable and reproducible AND they answer the original question. They come from experiments that were designed to be a FAIR TEST...

To Make an Investigation a Fair Test You Have to Control the Variables

1) In a lab experiment you usually change one variable and measure how it affects another variable.

2) To make it a fair test, everything else that could affect the results should stay the same — otherwise you can't tell if the thing you're changing is causing the results or not.

3) The variable you CHANGE is called the INDEPENDENT variable.

4) The variable you MEASURE when you change the independent variable is the DEPENDENT variable.

5) The variables that you KEEP THE SAME are called CONTROL variables.

> You could find how temperature affects reaction rate by measuring the volume of gas formed over time. The independent variable is the temperature. The dependent variable is the volume of gas produced. Control variables include the concentration and amounts of reactants, the time period you measure, etc.

6) Because you can't always control all the variables, you often need to use a control experiment. This is an experiment that's kept under the same conditions as the rest of the investigation, but doesn't have anything done to it. This is so that you can see what happens when you don't change anything at all.

The Bigger the Sample Size the Better

1) Data based on small samples isn't as good as data based on large samples. A sample should represent the whole population (i.e. it should share as many of the characteristics in the population as possible) — a small sample can't do that as well. It's also harder to spot anomalies if your sample size is too small.

2) The bigger the sample size the better, but scientists have to be realistic when choosing how big. For example, if you were studying the effects of a chemical used to sterilise water on the people drinking it, it'd be great to study everyone who was drinking the water (a huge sample), but it'd take ages and cost a bomb. It's more realistic to study a thousand people, with a mixture of ages, gender, and race.

This is no high street survey — it's a designer investigation...

Not only do you need to be able to plan your own investigations, you should also be able to look at someone else's plan and decide whether or not it needs improving. Those examiners aren't half demanding.

Collecting Data

You've designed the perfect investigation — now it's time to get your hands mucky and collect some data.

Your Data Should be Repeatable, Reproducible, Accurate and Precise

1) To check repeatability you need to repeat the readings and check that the results are similar. You need to repeat each reading at least three times.

2) To make sure your results are reproducible you can cross check them by taking a second set of readings with another instrument (or a different observer).

3) Your data also needs to be ACCURATE. Really accurate results are those that are really close to the true answer. The accuracy of your results usually depends on your method — you need to make sure you're measuring the right thing and that you don't miss anything that should be included in the measurements. E.g. estimating the amount of gas released from a reaction by counting the bubbles isn't very accurate because you might miss some of the bubbles and they might have different volumes. It's more accurate to measure the volume of gas released using a gas syringe (see p.107).

Brian's result was a curate.

Repeat	Data set 1	Data set 2
1	12	11
2	14	17
3	13	14
Mean	13	14

Data set 1 is more precise than data set 2.

4) Your data also needs to be PRECISE. Precise results are ones where the data is all really close to the mean (average) of your repeated results (i.e. not spread out).

Your Equipment has to be Right for the Job

1) The measuring equipment you use has to be sensitive enough to measure the changes you're looking for. For example, if you need to measure changes of 1 cm^3 you need to use a measuring cylinder or burette that can measure in 1 cm^3 steps — it'd be no good trying with one that only measures 10 cm^3 steps.

2) The smallest change a measuring instrument can detect is called its RESOLUTION. E.g. some mass balances have a resolution of 1 g, some have a resolution of 0.1 g, and some are even more sensitive.

3) Also, equipment needs to be calibrated by measuring a known value. If there's a difference between the measured and known value, you can use this to correct the inaccuracy of the equipment.

You Need to Look out for Errors and Anomalous Results

1) The results of your experiment will always vary a bit because of RANDOM ERRORS — unpredictable differences caused by things like human errors in measuring. The errors when you make a reading from a burette are random. You have to estimate or round the level when it's between two marks — so sometimes your figure will be a bit above the real one, and sometimes it will be a bit below.

2) You can reduce the effect of random errors by taking repeat readings and finding the mean. This will make your results more precise.

3) If a measurement is wrong by the same amount every time, it's called a SYSTEMATIC ERROR. For example, if you measured from the very end of your ruler instead of from the 0 cm mark every time, all your measurements would be a bit small. Repeating the experiment in the exact same way and calculating a mean won't correct a systematic error.

If there's no systematic error, then doing repeats and calculating a mean can make your results more accurate.

4) Just to make things more complicated, if a systematic error is caused by using equipment that isn't zeroed properly, it's called a ZERO ERROR. For example, if a mass balance always reads 1 gram before you put anything on it, all your measurements will be 1 gram too heavy.

5) You can compensate for some systematic errors if you know about them though, e.g. if your mass balance always reads 1 gram before you put anything on it you can subtract 1 gram from all your results.

6) Sometimes you get a result that doesn't fit in with the rest at all. This is called an ANOMALOUS RESULT. You should investigate it and try to work out what happened. If you can work out what happened (e.g. you measured something totally wrong) you can ignore it when processing your results.

Watch what you say to that mass balance — it's very sensitive...

Weirdly, data can be really precise but not very accurate. For example, a fancy piece of lab equipment might give results that are really precise, but if it's not been calibrated properly those results won't be accurate.

Processing and Presenting Data

Processing your data means doing some <u>calculations</u> with it to make it <u>more useful</u>. Once you've done that, you can present your results in a nice <u>chart</u> or <u>graph</u> to help you <u>spot any patterns</u> in your data.

Data Needs to be Organised

1) Tables are dead useful for <u>organising data</u>.

2) When you draw a table <u>use a ruler</u> and make sure <u>each column</u> has a <u>heading</u> (including the <u>units</u>).

You Might Have to Process Your Data

1) When you've done repeats of an experiment you should always calculate the <u>mean</u> (average). To do this <u>add together</u> all the data values and <u>divide</u> by the total number of values in the sample.

2) You might also need to calculate the <u>range</u> (how spread out the data is). To do this find the <u>largest</u> number and <u>subtract</u> the <u>smallest</u> number from it.

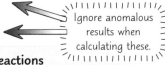
Ignore anomalous results when calculating these.

EXAMPLE: The results of an experiment to find the mass of gas lost from two reactions are shown below. Calculate the mean and the range for the mass of gas lost in each reaction.

Test tube	Repeat 1 (g)	Repeat 2 (g)	Repeat 3 (g)	Mean (g)	Range (g)
A	28	37	32	(28 + 37 + 32) ÷ 3 = 32	37 − 28 = 9
B	47	51	60	(47 + 51 + 60) ÷ 3 = 53	60 − 47 = 13

Round to the Lowest Number of Significant Figures

The <u>first significant figure</u> of a number is the first digit that's <u>not zero</u>. The second and third significant figures come <u>straight after</u> (even if they're zeros). You should be aware of significant figures in calculations.

1) In <u>any</u> calculation, you should round the answer to the <u>lowest number of significant figures</u> (s.f.) given.

2) Remember to write down <u>how many</u> significant figures you've rounded to after your answer.

3) If your calculation has multiple steps, <u>only</u> round the <u>final</u> answer, or it won't be as accurate.

EXAMPLE: The volume of one mole of gas is 24.0 dm^3 at room temperature and pressure. How many moles are there in 4.6 dm^3 of gas under the same conditions?

No. of moles of gas = 4.6 dm^3 ÷ 24.0 dm^3 = 0.19166... = 0.19 mol (2 s.f.)

2 s.f.   3 s.f.   Final answer should be rounded to 2 s.f.

If Your Data Comes in Categories, Present It in a Bar Chart

1) If the independent variable is <u>categoric</u> (comes in distinct categories, e.g. alkane chain length, metals) you should use a <u>bar chart</u> to display the data.

2) You also use them if the independent variable is <u>discrete</u> (the data can be counted in chunks, where there's no in-between value, e.g. number of protons is discrete because you can't have half a proton).

3) There are some <u>golden rules</u> you need to follow for <u>drawing</u> bar charts:

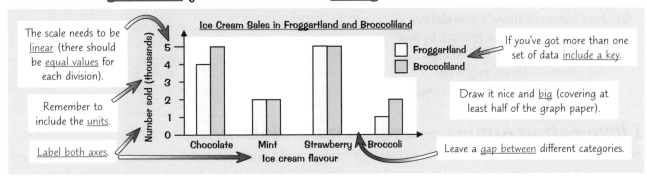

The scale needs to be <u>linear</u> (there should be <u>equal values</u> for each division).

Remember to include the <u>units</u>.

<u>Label both axes.</u>

Ice Cream Sales in Froggartland and Broccoliland

Number sold (thousands)

Chocolate   Mint   Strawberry   Broccoli
Ice cream flavour

Froggartland
Broccoliland

If you've got more than one set of data <u>include a key</u>.

Draw it nice and <u>big</u> (covering at least half of the graph paper).

Leave a <u>gap between</u> different categories.

If Your Data is Continuous, Plot a Graph

If both variables are <u>continuous</u> (numerical data that can have any value within a range, e.g. length, volume, temperature) you should use a <u>graph</u> to display the data.

Here are the rules for plotting points on a graph:

Use the biggest data values you've got to draw a <u>sensible scale</u> on your axes. Here, the highest amount of product formed is <u>8.8 cm³</u>, so it makes sense to label the y-axis up to <u>10 cm³</u>.

The <u>dependent</u> variable goes on the <u>y-axis</u> (the <u>vertical</u> one).

The <u>independent</u> variable goes on the <u>x-axis</u> (the <u>horizontal</u> one).

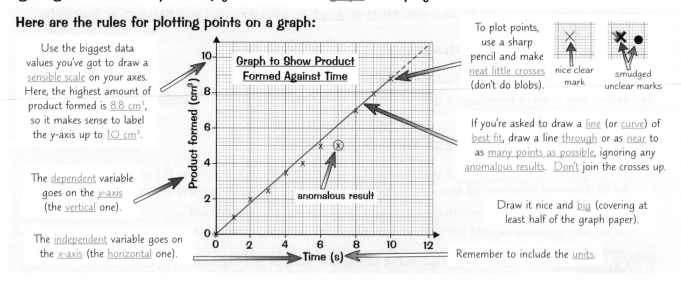

Graph to Show Product Formed Against Time

Product formed (cm³) — y-axis labelled 0, 2, 4, 6, 8, 10
Time (s) — x-axis labelled 0, 2, 4, 6, 8, 10, 12

anomalous result

To plot points, use a sharp pencil and make <u>neat little crosses</u> (don't do blobs).

nice clear mark — smudged unclear marks

If you're asked to draw a <u>line</u> (or <u>curve</u>) of <u>best fit</u>, draw a line <u>through</u> or as <u>near</u> to as <u>many points as possible</u>, ignoring any <u>anomalous results</u>. <u>Don't</u> join the crosses up.

Draw it nice and <u>big</u> (covering at least half of the graph paper).

Remember to include the <u>units</u>.

Graphs Can Give You a Lot of Information About Your Data

1) The <u>gradient</u> (slope) of a graph tells you how quickly the <u>dependent variable</u> changes if you change the <u>independent variable</u>.

$$\text{gradient} = \frac{\text{change in } y}{\text{change in } x}$$

This <u>graph</u> shows the <u>volume of gas</u> produced in a reaction against <u>time</u>. The graph is <u>linear</u> (it's a straight line graph), so you can simply calculate the <u>gradient</u> of the line to find out the <u>rate of reaction</u>.

1) To calculate the gradient, pick <u>two points</u> on the line that are easy to read and a <u>good distance</u> apart.

2) <u>Draw a line down</u> from one of the points and a <u>line across</u> from the other to make a <u>triangle</u>. The line drawn down the side of the triangle is the <u>change in y</u> and the line across the bottom is the <u>change in x</u>.

Change in y = 6.8 − 2.0 = 4.8 cm³   Change in x = 5.2 − 1.6 = 3.6 s

$$\text{Rate} = \text{gradient} = \frac{\text{change in } y}{\text{change in } x} = \frac{4.8 \text{ cm}^3}{3.6 \text{ s}} = \underline{1.3 \text{ cm}^3/\text{s}}$$

Volume of gas (cm³) — y-axis labelled 0, 2, 4, 6, 8
Time (s) — x-axis labelled 0, 2, 4, 6, 8
change in y — change in x

You can use this method to calculate other rates from a graph, not just the rate of a reaction. Just remember that a rate is how much something changes over time, so x needs to be the time.

The units of the gradient are (units of y)/(units of x). cm³/s can also be written as cm³s⁻¹.

2) To find the <u>gradient of a curve</u> at a <u>certain point</u>, draw a <u>tangent</u> to the curve at that point and then find the <u>gradient of the tangent</u>. See page 71 for details on how to do this.

3) The <u>intercept</u> of a graph is where the line of best fit crosses one of the <u>axes</u>. The <u>x-intercept</u> is where the line of best fit crosses the x-axis and the <u>y-intercept</u> is where it crosses the <u>y-axis</u>.

Graphs Show the Relationship Between Two Variables

1) You can get <u>three</u> types of <u>correlation</u> (relationship) between variables:

2) Just because there's correlation, it doesn't mean the change in one variable is <u>causing</u> the change in the other — there might be <u>other factors</u> involved (see page 10).

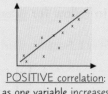

<u>POSITIVE</u> correlation: as one variable <u>increases</u> the other <u>increases</u>.

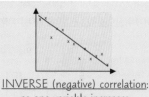

<u>INVERSE</u> (negative) correlation: as one variable <u>increases</u> the other <u>decreases</u>.

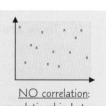

<u>NO</u> correlation: <u>no relationship</u> between the two variables.

I love eating apples — I call it core elation...

Science is all about finding relationships between things. And I don't mean that chemists gather together in corners to discuss whether or not Devini and Sebastian might be a couple... though they probably do that too.

Units and Equations

Graphs and maths skills are all very well, but the numbers don't mean much if you can't get the <u>units</u> right.

S.I. Units Are Used All Round the World

1) It wouldn't be all that useful if I defined volume in terms of <u>bath tubs</u>, you defined it in terms of <u>egg-cups</u> and my pal Sarwat defined it in terms of <u>balloons</u> — we'd never be able to compare our data.

2) To stop this happening, scientists have come up with a set of <u>standard units</u>, called S.I. units, that all scientists use to measure their data. Here are some S.I. units you'll see in chemistry:

Quantity	S.I. Base Unit
mass	kilogram, kg
length	metre, m
time	second, s
amount of a substance	mole, mol

Scaling Prefixes Can Be Used for Large and Small Quantities

1) Quantities come in a huge <u>range</u> of sizes. For example, the volume of a swimming pool might be around 2 000 000 000 cm^3, while the volume of a cup is around 250 cm^3.

2) To make the size of numbers more <u>manageable</u>, larger or smaller units are used. These are the <u>S.I. base unit</u> (e.g. metres) with a <u>prefix</u> in front:

prefix	tera (T)	giga (G)	mega (M)	kilo (k)	deci (d)	centi (c)	milli (m)	micro (μ)	nano (n)
multiple of unit	10^{12}	10^9	1 000 000 (10^6)	1000	0.1	0.01	0.001	0.000001 (10^{-6})	10^{-9}

3) These <u>prefixes</u> tell you <u>how much bigger</u> or <u>smaller</u> a unit is than the base unit. So one <u>kilometre</u> is <u>one thousand</u> metres.

The conversion factor is the number of times the smaller unit goes into the larger unit.

4) To <u>swap</u> from one unit to another, all you need to know is what number you have to divide or multiply by to get from the original unit to the new unit — this is called the <u>conversion factor</u>.

- To go from a <u>bigger unit</u> (like m) to a <u>smaller unit</u> (like cm), you <u>multiply</u> by the conversion factor.
- To go from a <u>smaller unit</u> (like g) to a <u>bigger unit</u> (like kg), you <u>divide</u> by the conversion factor.

5) Here are some conversions that'll be useful for GCSE chemistry:

Mass can have units of kg and g.
kg ×1000 → g, g ÷1000 → kg

Energy can have units of J and kJ.
kJ ×1000 → J, J ÷1000 → kJ

Volume can have units of m^3, dm^3 and cm^3.
m^3 ×1000 → dm^3, dm^3 ×1000 → cm^3, ÷1000, ÷1000

Concentration can have units of mol/dm^3 and mol/cm^3.
mol/dm^3 ÷1000 → mol/cm^3, ×1000

Always Check The Values Used in Equations Have the Right Units

1) Formulas and equations show <u>relationships</u> between <u>variables</u>.

2) To <u>rearrange</u> an equation, make sure that whatever you do to <u>one side</u> of the equation you also do to the <u>other side</u>.

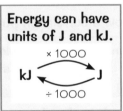

> You can find the <u>number of moles</u> of something using the equation: moles = mass ÷ molar mass.
> You can <u>rearrange</u> this equation to find the <u>mass</u> by <u>multiplying each side</u> by molar mass to give: mass = moles × molar mass.

3) To use a formula, you need to know the values of <u>all but one</u> of the variables. <u>Substitute</u> the values you do know into the formula, and do the calculation to work out the final variable.

4) Always make sure the values you put into an equation or formula have the <u>right units</u>. For example, you might have done a titration experiment to work out the concentration of a solution. The volume of the solution will probably have been measured in cm^3, but the equation to find concentration uses volume in dm^3. So you'll have to <u>convert</u> your volume from cm^3 to dm^3 before you put it into the equation.

5) To make sure your units are <u>correct</u>, it can help to write down the <u>units</u> on each line of your <u>calculation</u>.

I wasn't sure I liked units, but now I'm converted...

It's easy to get in a muddle when converting between units, but there's a handy way to check you've done it right. If you're moving from a smaller unit to a larger unit (e.g. g to kg) the number should get smaller, and vice versa.

Drawing Conclusions

Congratulations — you're nearly at the end of a gruelling investigation, time to <u>draw conclusions</u>.

You Can Only Conclude What the Data Shows and NO MORE

1) Drawing conclusions might seem pretty straightforward — you just <u>look at your data</u> and <u>say what pattern or relationship you see</u> between the dependent and independent variables.

The table on the right shows the rate of a reaction in the presence of two <u>different</u> catalysts:

Catalyst	Rate of reaction (cm³/s)
A	13.5
B	19.5
No catalyst	5.5

<u>CONCLUSION:</u>
Catalyst <u>B</u> makes <u>this reaction</u> go faster than catalyst A.

2) But you've got to be really careful that your conclusion <u>matches the data</u> you've got and <u>doesn't go any further</u>.

You <u>can't</u> conclude that catalyst B increases the rate of <u>any other reaction</u> more than catalyst A — the results might be completely different.

3) You also need to be able to <u>use your results</u> to <u>justify your conclusion</u> (i.e. back up your conclusion with some specific data).

The rate of this reaction was <u>6 cm³/s faster</u> using catalyst B compared with catalyst A.

4) When writing a conclusion you need to <u>refer back</u> to the original hypothesis and say whether the data <u>supports it</u> or not:

The hypothesis for this experiment might have been that catalyst B would make the reaction go <u>quicker</u> than catalyst A. If so, the data <u>supports</u> the hypothesis.

Correlation DOES NOT Mean Cause

If two things are correlated (i.e. there's a relationship between them) it <u>doesn't</u> necessarily mean a change in one variable is <u>causing</u> the change in the other — this is <u>REALLY IMPORTANT</u> — <u>DON'T FORGET IT</u>. There are <u>three possible reasons</u> for a correlation:

1) <u>CHANCE:</u> It might seem strange, but two things can show a correlation purely due to <u>chance</u>.

For example, one study might find a correlation between people's hair colour and how good they are at frisbee. But other scientists <u>don't</u> get a correlation when they investigate it — the results of the first study are just a <u>fluke</u>.

2) <u>LINKED BY A 3RD VARIABLE:</u> A lot of the time it may <u>look</u> as if a change in one variable is causing a change in the other, but it <u>isn't</u> — a <u>third variable links</u> the two things.

For example, there's a correlation between <u>water temperature</u> and <u>shark attacks</u>. This isn't because warmer water makes sharks crazy. Instead, they're linked by a third variable — the <u>number of people swimming</u> (more people swim when the water's hotter, and with more people in the water you get more shark attacks).

3) <u>CAUSE:</u> Sometimes a change in one variable does <u>cause</u> a change in the other. You can only conclude that a correlation is due to cause when you've <u>controlled all the variables</u> that could, just could, be affecting the result.

For example, there's a correlation between <u>smoking</u> and <u>lung cancer</u>. This is because chemicals in tobacco smoke cause lung cancer. This conclusion was only made once <u>other variables</u> (such as age and exposure to other things that cause cancer) had been <u>controlled</u> and shown <u>not</u> to affect people's risk of getting lung cancer.

I conclude that this page is a bit dull...

...although, just because I find it dull doesn't mean that I can conclude it's dull (you might think it's the most interesting thing since that kid got his head stuck in the railings near school). In the exams you could be given a conclusion and asked whether some data supports it — so make sure you understand how far conclusions can go.

Uncertainties and Evaluations

Hurrah! The end of another investigation. Well, now you have to work out all the things you did <u>wrong</u>.

Uncertainty is the Amount of Error Your Measurements Might Have

1) When you <u>repeat</u> a measurement, you often get a <u>slightly different</u> figure each time you do it due to <u>random error</u>. This means that <u>each result</u> has some <u>uncertainty</u> to it.

2) The measurements you make will also have some uncertainty in them due to <u>limits</u> in the <u>resolution</u> of the equipment you use (see page 6).

3) This all means that the <u>mean</u> of a set of results will also have some uncertainty to it. You can calculate the uncertainty of a <u>mean result</u> using the equation:

4) The <u>larger</u> the range, the <u>less precise</u> your results are and the <u>more uncertainty</u> there will be in your results. Uncertainties are shown using the '±' symbol.

The range is the largest value minus the smallest value (p.7).

$$\text{uncertainty} = \frac{\text{range}}{2}$$

 **EXAMPLE:**   The table below shows the results of a titration experiment to determine the volume of 0.5 mol/dm³ sodium hydroxide solution needed to neutralise 25 cm³ of a solution of hydrochloric acid with unknown concentration. Calculate the uncertainty of the mean.

Repeat	1	2	3	mean
Volume of sodium hydroxide (cm³)	20.10	19.80	20.00	19.97

1) First work out the range:
Range = 20.10 − 19.80
= 0.300 cm³

2) Use the range to find the uncertainty:
Uncertainty = range ÷ 2 = 0.300 ÷ 2 = 0.150 cm³   So the uncertainty of the mean = 19.97 ± 0.15 cm³

5) Measuring a <u>greater amount</u> of something helps to <u>reduce uncertainty</u>. For example, in a rate of reaction experiment, measuring the amount of product formed over a <u>longer period</u> compared to a shorter period will <u>reduce</u> the <u>percentage uncertainty</u> in your results.

Evaluations — Describe How it Could be Improved

An evaluation is a <u>critical analysis</u> of the whole investigation.

I'd value this E somewhere in the region of 250-300k.

1) You should comment on the <u>method</u> — was it <u>valid</u>? Did you control all the other variables to make it a <u>fair test</u>?

2) Comment on the <u>quality</u> of the <u>results</u> — was there <u>enough evidence</u> to reach a valid <u>conclusion</u>? Were the results <u>repeatable</u>, <u>reproducible</u>, <u>accurate</u> and <u>precise</u>?

3) Were there any <u>anomalous</u> results? If there were <u>none</u> then <u>say so</u>. If there were any, try to <u>explain</u> them — were they caused by <u>errors</u> in measurement? Were there any other <u>variables</u> that could have <u>affected</u> the results? You should comment on the level of <u>uncertainty</u> in your results too.

4) All this analysis will allow you to say how <u>confident</u> you are that your conclusion is <u>right</u>.

5) Then you can suggest any <u>changes</u> to the <u>method</u> that would <u>improve</u> the quality of the results, so that you could have <u>more confidence</u> in your conclusion. For example, you might suggest <u>changing</u> the way you controlled a variable, or <u>increasing</u> the number of <u>measurements</u> you took. Taking more measurements at <u>narrower intervals</u> could give you a <u>more accurate result</u>. For example:

<u>Enzymes</u> have an <u>optimum temperature</u> (a temperature at which they <u>work best</u>). Say you do an experiment to find an enzyme's optimum temperature and take measurements at 10 °C, 20 °C, 30 °C, 40 °C and 50 °C. The results of this experiment tell you the optimum is <u>40 °C</u>. You could then <u>repeat</u> the experiment, taking <u>more measurements around 40 °C</u> to a get a <u>more accurate</u> value for the optimum.

6) You could also make more <u>predictions</u> based on your conclusion, then <u>further experiments</u> could be carried out to test them.

When suggesting improvements to the investigation, always make sure that you say why you think this would make the results better.

Evaluation — next time, I'll make sure I don't burn the lab down...

So there you have it — Working Scientifically. Make sure you know this stuff like the back of your hand. It's not just in the lab that you'll need to know how to work scientifically. You can be asked about it in the exams as well.

Atoms

All substances are made of <u>atoms</u>. They're really <u>tiny</u> — too small to see, even with your microscope. Atoms are so tiny that a <u>50p piece</u> contains about 77 400 000 000 000 000 000 000 of them. Quite a lot then...

Atoms Contain Protons, Neutrons and Electrons

Atoms have a radius of about <u>0.1 nanometers</u> (that's 1×10^{-10} m). There are a few different (and equally useful) modern models of the atom — but chemists tend to like the model below best.

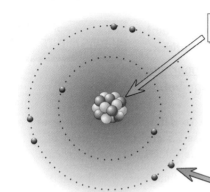

The Nucleus

1) It's in the <u>middle</u> of the atom.
2) It contains <u>protons</u> and <u>neutrons</u>.
3) The nucleus has a <u>radius</u> of around 1×10^{-14} m (that's around 1/10 000 of the radius of an atom)
4) It has a <u>positive charge</u> because of the protons.
5) Almost the <u>whole</u> mass of the atom is <u>concentrated</u> in the nucleus.

> A nanometer (nm) is one billionth of a meter. Shown in standard form, that's 1×10^{-9} m. Standard form is used for showing really large or really small numbers.

Protons are heavy and positively charged.
Neutrons are heavy and neutral.
Electrons are tiny and negatively charged.

Particle	Relative Mass	Charge
Proton	1	+1
Neutron	1	0
Electron	Very small	–1

(<u>Electron mass</u> is often taken as <u>zero</u>.)

The Electrons

1) Move <u>around</u> the nucleus in electron <u>shells</u>.
2) They're <u>negatively charged</u> and <u>tiny</u>, but they cover <u>a lot of space</u>.
3) The <u>volume</u> of their orbits determines the size of the atom.
4) Electrons have virtually <u>no</u> mass.

Number of Protons Equals Number of Electrons

1) Atoms are <u>neutral</u> — they have <u>no charge</u> overall (unlike ions).
2) This is because they have the <u>same number</u> of <u>protons</u> as <u>electrons</u>.
3) The <u>charge</u> on the electrons is the <u>same</u> size as the charge on the <u>protons</u>, but <u>opposite</u> — so the charges <u>cancel out</u>.
4) In an ion, the number of protons <u>doesn't equal</u> the number of <u>electrons</u>. This means it has an <u>overall charge</u>. For example, an ion with a <u>2– charge</u>, has <u>two more</u> electrons than protons.

> An ion is an atom or group of atoms that has lost or gained electrons.

Atomic Number and Mass Number Describe an Atom

1) The <u>nuclear symbol</u> of an atom tells you its <u>atomic (proton) number</u> and <u>mass number</u>.
2) The <u>atomic number</u> tells you how many <u>protons</u> there are.
3) The <u>mass number</u> tells you the <u>total number</u> of <u>protons and neutrons</u> in the atom.
4) To get the number of <u>neutrons</u>, just subtract the <u>atomic number</u> from the <u>mass number</u>.

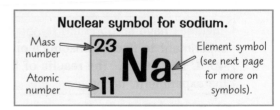

Nuclear symbol for sodium.

Mass number → **23**
Atomic number → **11** **Na**
Element symbol (see next page for more on symbols).

Let's be positive about this — unless you're an electron of course...

So here we are — the very beginning of GCSE Chemistry. This stuff is super important — if you get to grips with the basic facts then you'll have a better chance understanding the rest of chemistry. Crack on.

Q1   An atom of nitrogen has an atomic number of 7 and a mass number of 14.
     Give the number of electrons, protons and neutrons in the atom.

[3 marks]

Elements

An <u>element</u> is a substance made up of atoms that all have the <u>same</u> number of <u>protons</u> in their nucleus.

Elements Consist of Atoms With the Same Atomic Number

1) Atoms can have different numbers of protons, neutrons and electrons.
   It's the number of <u>protons</u> in the nucleus that decides what <u>type</u> of atom it is.

2) For example, an atom with <u>one proton</u> in its nucleus is <u>hydrogen</u> and an atom with <u>two protons</u> is <u>helium</u>.

3) If a substance only contains atoms with the <u>same number</u> of <u>protons</u> it's called an <u>element</u>.
   There are about <u>100 different elements</u>.

4) So <u>all the atoms</u> of a particular <u>element</u> (e.g. nitrogen) have the <u>same number</u> of
   protons and <u>different elements</u> have atoms with <u>different numbers</u> of protons.

Atoms Can be Represented by Symbols

Atoms of each element can be represented by a <u>one or two letter symbol</u> — it's a type of <u>shorthand</u>
that saves you the bother of having to write the full name of the element.

Some make <u>perfect sense</u>, e.g. | C = carbon   O = oxygen   Mg = magnesium |

Others less so, e.g. | Na = sodium   Fe = iron   Pb = lead | Most of these odd symbols actually come from the Latin names of the elements.

You'll see these symbols on the periodic table (see page 22).

Isotopes are the Same Except for Extra Neutrons

1) <u>Isotopes</u> are different forms of the same element, which have
   the <u>same number</u> of <u>protons</u> but a <u>different number</u> of <u>neutrons</u>.

2) So isotopes have the <u>same atomic number</u> but <u>different mass numbers</u>.

The number of neutrons is just the mass number minus the atomic number.

3) A very popular example of a pair of isotopes are <u>carbon-12</u> and <u>carbon-13</u>.

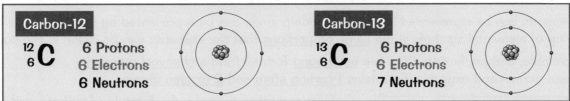

Carbon-12		Carbon-13	
$^{12}_{6}C$	6 Protons 6 Electrons 6 Neutrons	$^{13}_{6}C$	6 Protons 6 Electrons 7 Neutrons

4) Because many <u>elements</u> can exist as a number of different isotopes, <u>relative atomic mass</u> (A_r) is used
   instead of mass number when referring to the element as a whole. This is an <u>average</u> mass taking into
   account the <u>different masses</u> and <u>abundances</u> (amounts) of all the isotopes that make up the element.

5) You can use this <u>formula</u>
   to work out the <u>relative</u>
   <u>atomic mass</u> of an element: ⟹

$$\text{relative atomic mass } (A_r) = \frac{\text{sum of (isotope abundance} \times \text{isotope mass number)}}{\text{sum of abundances of all the isotopes}}$$

EXAMPLE: Copper has two stable isotopes. Cu-63 has an abundance of 69.2% and Cu-65 has an
abundance of 30.8%. Calculate the relative atomic mass of copper to 1 decimal place.

$$\text{Relative atomic mass} = \frac{(69.2 \times 63) + (30.8 \times 65)}{69.2 + 30.8} = \frac{4359.6 + 2002}{100} = \frac{6361.6}{100} = 63.616 = 63.6$$

It's elemental my dear Watson...

Atoms, elements and isotopes — make sure you know what they are and the differences between them.

Q1   A substance consists of atoms which all have the same number of protons and electrons
     but different numbers of neutrons. Explain why this substance is an element.   [1 mark]

Q2   An isotope of iron, Fe, has a <u>mass number of 56</u> and <u>atomic number 26</u>.
     Give the number of protons and neutrons in an atom of this isotope.   [2 marks]

Compounds

It would be great if we only had to deal with elements. But unluckily for you, elements can mix and match to make lots of new substances called <u>compounds</u>. And this makes things a little bit more complicated...

Atoms Join Together to Make Compounds

1) When <u>elements react</u>, atoms <u>combine</u> with other atoms to form <u>compounds</u>.

2) Compounds are substances formed from <u>two or more</u> elements, the atoms of each are in <u>fixed proportions</u> throughout the compound and they're held together by <u>chemical bonds</u>.

3) <u>Making bonds</u> involves atoms giving away, taking or sharing <u>electrons</u>. Only the <u>electrons</u> are involved — the nuclei of the atoms aren't affected at all when a bond is made.

4) It's <u>usually difficult</u> to <u>separate</u> the original elements of a compound out again — a chemical reaction is needed to do this.

> During a chemical reaction, at least one new substance is made. You can usually measure a change in energy, such as a temperature change, as well.

5) A compound which is formed from a <u>metal</u> and a <u>non-metal</u> consists of <u>ions</u>. The <u>metal</u> atoms <u>lose</u> electrons to form <u>positive ions</u> and the non-metal atoms <u>gain</u> electrons to form <u>negative ions</u>. The <u>opposite charges</u> (positive and negative) of the ions mean that they're strongly <u>attracted</u> to each other. This is called <u>ionic bonding</u>. Examples of compounds which are bonded ionically include sodium chloride, magnesium oxide and calcium oxide.

6) A compound formed from <u>non-metals</u> consists of <u>molecules</u>. Each atom <u>shares</u> an <u>electron</u> with another atom — this is called <u>covalent bonding</u>. Examples of compounds that are bonded covalently include hydrogen chloride gas, carbon monoxide, and water.

7) The <u>properties</u> of a compound are usually <u>totally different</u> from the properties of the <u>original elements</u>. For example, if iron (a lustrous magnetic metal) and sulfur (a nice yellow powder) react, the compound formed (<u>iron sulfide</u>) is a <u>dull grey solid lump</u>, and doesn't behave <u>anything like</u> either iron or sulfur.

Heat

Fe + S → Fe S FeS

Mixture   Compound

A Formula Shows What Atoms are in a Compound

Just as elements can be represented by <u>symbols</u>, compounds can be represented by <u>formulas</u>. The formulas are made up of elemental symbols in the <u>same proportions</u> that the elements can be found in the compound.

1) For example, carbon dioxide, CO_2, is a <u>compound</u> formed from a <u>chemical reaction</u> between carbon and oxygen. It contains <u>1 carbon atom</u> and <u>2 oxygen atoms</u>.

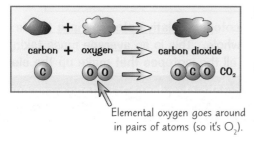

carbon + oxygen ⟹ carbon dioxide

C + O O ⟹ O C O CO_2

Elemental oxygen goes around in pairs of atoms (so it's O_2).

2) Here's another example: the formula of <u>sulfuric acid</u> is H_2SO_4. So, each molecule contains <u>2 hydrogen atoms</u>, <u>1 sulfur atom</u> and <u>4 oxygen atoms</u>.

3) There might be <u>brackets</u> in a formula, e.g. calcium hydroxide is $Ca(OH)_2$. The little number outside the bracket applies to <u>everything</u> inside the brackets. So in $Ca(OH)_2$ there's <u>1 calcium atom</u>, <u>2 oxygen atoms</u> and <u>2 hydrogen atoms</u>.

Here are some examples of formulas which might come in handy:

1) Carbon dioxide — CO_2	4) Sodium chloride — $NaCl$	7) Calcium chloride — $CaCl_2$
2) Ammonia — NH_3	5) Carbon monoxide — CO	8) Sodium carbonate — Na_2CO_3
3) Water — H_2O	6) Hydrochloric acid — HCl	9) Sulfuric acid — H_2SO_4

If you don't learn this stuff it will only compound your problems...

You know when you were little and taught to share things? Turns out atoms have been doing this since the start of the universe. Maybe we could all learn a thing or two from those little guys.

Q1   How many atoms are in one particle of Na_2CO_3?   [1 mark]

Q2   A compound has the formula $CaCl_2$. Name the compound and the elements it contains.   [2 marks]

Chemical Equations

Chemical equations are fundamental to chemistry. Pretty much like tomato ketchup is to a bacon butty. Mmm... bacon butties... Sorry, I got distracted. Let's do this.

Chemical Changes are Shown Using Chemical Equations

One way to show a chemical reaction is to write a word equation. It's not as quick as using chemical symbols and you can't tell straight away what's happened to each of the atoms, but it's dead easy.

Here's an example — you're told that methane burns in oxygen giving carbon dioxide and water:

The molecules on the left-hand side of the equation are called the reactants (because they react with each other).

methane + oxygen → carbon dioxide + water

The molecules on the right-hand side are called the products (because they've been produced from the reactants).

Symbol Equations Show the Atoms on Both Sides

Chemical changes can be shown in a kind of shorthand using symbol equations. Symbol equations just show the symbols or formulas of the reactants and products...

magnesium + oxygen → magnesium oxide
$2Mg + O_2$ → $2MgO$

You'll have spotted that there's a '2' in front of the Mg and the MgO. The reason for this is explained below...

Symbol Equations Need to be Balanced

1) There must always be the same number of atoms on both sides — they can't just disappear.

2) You balance the equation by putting numbers in front of the formulas where needed. Take this equation for reacting sulfuric acid with sodium hydroxide:

$$H_2SO_4 + NaOH \rightarrow Na_2SO_4 + H_2O$$

3) The formulas are all correct but the numbers of some atoms don't match up on both sides.

$E=mc^2$

4) You can't change formulas like H_2SO_4 to H_2SO_5. You can only put numbers in front of them.

The more you practise, the quicker you get, but all you do is this:

1) Find an element that doesn't balance and pencil in a number to try and sort it out.

2) See where it gets you. It may create another imbalance, but if so, pencil in another number and see where that gets you.

3) Carry on chasing unbalanced elements and it'll sort itself out pretty quickly.

EXAMPLE: In the equation above you'll notice we're short of H atoms on the RHS (Right-Hand Side).

1) The only thing you can do about that is make it $2H_2O$ instead of just H_2O:

$$H_2SO_4 + NaOH \rightarrow Na_2SO_4 + 2H_2O$$

2) But that now gives too many H atoms and O atoms on the RHS, so to balance that up you could try putting $2NaOH$ on the LHS (Left-Hand Side):

$$H_2SO_4 + 2NaOH \rightarrow Na_2SO_4 + 2H_2O$$

3) And suddenly there it is! Everything balances. And you'll notice the Na just sorted itself out.

Revision is all about getting the balance right...

Balancing equations is all about practice. Once you have a few goes you'll see it's much less scary than it seemed before you took on, challenged and defeated this page. Go grab some chemistry glory.

Q1 Balance the equation: $Fe + Cl_2 \rightarrow FeCl_3$ [1 mark]

Q2 Hydrogen and oxygen molecules are formed in a reaction where water splits apart.
For this reaction: a) State the word equation. b) Give a balanced symbol equation. [3 marks]

Mixtures and Chromatography

Mixtures in <u>chemistry</u> are just like mixtures in baking, lots of <u>separate</u> things all mixed together. But most of the time they're considerably less delicious. And you probably shouldn't eat them. Or put them in an oven.

Mixtures are Easily Separated — Not Like Compounds

1) Unlike in a compound, there's <u>no chemical bond</u> between the different parts of a mixture.

2) The parts of a mixture can be either <u>elements</u> or <u>compounds</u>, and they can be separated out by <u>physical methods</u> such as filtration (p. 17), crystallisation (p.17), simple distillation (p.18), fractional distillation (p.18) and chromatography (see below).

3) <u>Air</u> is a <u>mixture</u> of gases, mainly nitrogen, oxygen, carbon dioxide and argon. The gases can all be <u>separated out</u> fairly easily.

4) <u>Crude oil</u> is a <u>mixture</u> of different length hydrocarbon molecules.

5) The <u>properties</u> of a mixture are just a <u>mixture</u> of the properties of the <u>separate parts</u> — the chemical properties of a substance <u>aren't</u> affected by it being part of a mixture.

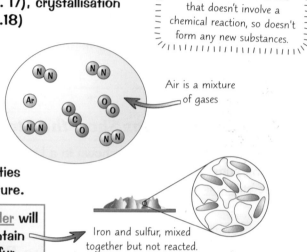

A physical method is one that doesn't involve a chemical reaction, so doesn't form any new substances.

Air is a mixture of gases

> For example, a <u>mixture</u> of <u>iron powder</u> and <u>sulfur powder</u> will show the properties of <u>both iron and sulfur</u>. It will contain grey magnetic bits of iron and bright yellow bits of sulfur.

Iron and sulfur, mixed together but not reacted.

You Need to Know How to Do Paper Chromatography

PRACTICAL

One method of separating substances in a mixture is through <u>chromatography</u>. This technique can be used to separate different <u>dyes</u> in an <u>ink</u>. Here's how you can do it:

1) Draw a <u>line</u> near the bottom of a sheet of <u>filter paper</u>. (Use a <u>pencil</u> to do this — pencil marks are <u>insoluble</u> and won't dissolve in the solvent.)

2) Add a <u>spot</u> of the ink to the line and place the sheet in a beaker of <u>solvent</u>, e.g water.

3) The <u>solvent</u> used depends on what's being tested. Some compounds <u>dissolve</u> well in <u>water</u>, but sometimes other solvents, like ethanol, are needed.

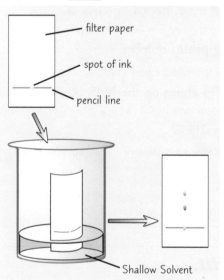

filter paper

spot of ink

pencil line

Shallow Solvent

4) Make sure the ink isn't touching the solvent — you don't want it to <u>dissolve</u> into it.

5) Place a <u>lid</u> on top of the container to stop the solvent <u>evaporating</u>.

6) The solvent <u>seeps</u> up the paper, carrying the ink with it.

7) Each different <u>dye</u> in the ink will move up the paper at a <u>different rate</u> so the dyes will <u>separate out</u>. Each dye will form a <u>spot</u> in a different place — 1 spot per dye in the ink.

8) If any of the dyes in the ink are <u>insoluble</u> (won't dissolve) in the solvent you've used, they'll stay on the <u>baseline</u>.

9) When the <u>solvent</u> has nearly reached the <u>top</u> of the paper, take the paper out of the beaker and leave it to <u>dry</u>.

The point the solvent has reached as it moves up the paper is the solvent front.

10) The end result is a pattern of spots called a <u>chromatogram</u>.

Chemistry and fun are a mixture — easily separated...

Chromatography is actually mighty useful in real life. It's used to test athletes' urine samples for performance enhancing drugs, and also to test unknown substances at crime scenes. Eeek...

Q1 Explain why you shouldn't use a pen to draw a line on the filter paper for paper chromatography. [1 mark]

More Separation Techniques

Filtration and crystallisation are <u>methods</u> of <u>separating mixtures</u>. Chemists use these techniques all the time to separate <u>solids</u> from <u>liquids</u>, so it's worth making sure you know how to do them.

Filtration Separates Insoluble Solids from Liquids

1) Filtration can be used if your <u>product</u> is an <u>insoluble solid</u> that needs to be separated from a <u>liquid reaction mixture</u>.

2) It can be used in <u>purification</u> as well. For example, <u>solid impurities</u> in the reaction mixture can be separated out using <u>filtration</u>.

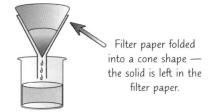

Filter paper folded into a cone shape — the solid is left in the filter paper.

⟍ Insoluble means the solid can't be dissolved in the liquid. ⟋

Two Ways to Separate Soluble Solids from Solutions

If a solid can be <u>dissolved</u> it's described as being <u>soluble</u>. There are <u>two</u> methods you can use to separate a soluble salt from a solution — <u>evaporation</u> and <u>crystallisation</u>.

Evaporation

evaporating dish

You don't have to use a Bunsen burner, you could use a water bath, or an electric heater.

1) Pour the solution into an <u>evaporating dish</u>.

2) Slowly <u>heat</u> the solution. The <u>solvent</u> will evaporate and the solution will get more <u>concentrated</u>. Eventually, <u>crystals</u> will start to form.

3) Keep heating the evaporating dish until all you have left are <u>dry crystals</u>.

Evaporation is a really <u>quick</u> way of separating a soluble salt from a solution, but you can only use it if the salt <u>doesn't decompose</u> (break down) when its heated. Otherwise, you'll have to use <u>crystallisation</u>.

Crystallisation

You should also use crystallisation if you want to make nice big crystals of your salt.

1) Pour the solution into an <u>evaporating dish</u> and gently <u>heat</u> the solution. Some of the <u>solvent</u> will evaporate and the solution will get more <u>concentrated</u>.

2) Once some of the solvent has evaporated, <u>or</u> when you see crystals start to form (the <u>point of crystallisation</u>), remove the dish from the heat and leave the solution to <u>cool</u>.

3) The salt should start to form <u>crystals</u> as it becomes <u>insoluble</u> in the cold, highly concentrated solution.

4) <u>Filter</u> the crystals out of the solution, and leave them in a warm place to <u>dry</u>. You could also use a <u>drying oven</u> or a <u>desiccator</u>.

Salt crystallising out of solution.

Filtration and Crystallisation can be Used to Separate Rock Salt

1) <u>Rock salt</u> is simply a <u>mixture</u> of <u>salt</u> and <u>sand</u> (they spread it on the roads in winter).

2) Salt and sand are both <u>compounds</u> — but <u>salt dissolves</u> in water and <u>sand doesn't</u>. This <u>vital difference</u> in their <u>physical properties</u> gives a great way to <u>separate</u> them. Here's what to do...

1) <u>Grind</u> the mixture to make sure the salt crystals are small, so will dissolve easily.

You can heat the mixture to help dissolve the salt.

2) Put the mixture in water and stir. The <u>salt</u> will <u>dissolve</u>, but the <u>sand won't</u>.

3) <u>Filter</u> the mixture. The grains of <u>sand</u> won't fit through the tiny holes in the filter paper, so they collect on the <u>paper</u> instead. The <u>salt</u> passes <u>through</u> the filter paper as it's part of the solution.

4) <u>Evaporate</u> the water from the salt so that it forms <u>dry crystals</u>.

You could also use crystallisation here if you wanted to make nice, big crystals.

Revise mixtures — just filter out the important bits...

Two out of three pages on separating mixtures done, phew... But before you dash on to the next page (I know, it's just so exciting), make sure you know this page to a T. Talking about Tea, I need a cuppa...

Q1 A student needs to produce pure crystals of copper sulfate from an aqueous solution of copper sulfate. Describe how the student could use crystallisation for this process. [4 marks]

Distillation

Distillation is used to separate mixtures which contain <u>liquids</u>. There are two types that you should know about — <u>simple</u> and <u>fractional</u>. Hopefully, this page will 'distil' everything you need to know... ho ho.

Simple Distillation is Used to Separate Out Solutions

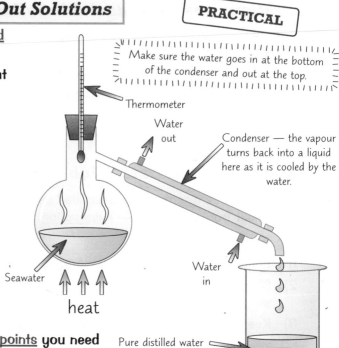

PRACTICAL

1) <u>Simple distillation</u> is used for separating out a <u>liquid</u> from a <u>solution</u>.

2) The solution is <u>heated</u>. The part of the solution that has the lowest boiling point <u>evaporates</u> first.

3) The <u>vapour</u> is then <u>cooled</u>, <u>condenses</u> (turns back into a liquid) and is <u>collected</u>.

4) The rest of the <u>solution</u> is left behind in the flask.

5) You can use simple distillation to get <u>pure water</u> from <u>seawater</u>. The <u>water</u> evaporates and is condensed and collected. Eventually you'll end up with just the <u>salt</u> left in the flask.

6) The <u>problem</u> with simple distillation is that you can only use it to separate things with <u>very different</u> boiling points — if the temperature goes higher than the boiling point of the substance with the higher boiling point, they will <u>mix</u> again.

7) If you have a <u>mixture of liquids</u> with <u>similar boiling points</u> you need another method to separate them — like fractional distillation...

Make sure the water goes in at the bottom of the condenser and out at the top.

Thermometer

Water out

Condenser — the vapour turns back into a liquid here as it is cooled by the water.

Seawater

Water in

heat

Pure distilled water

Fractional Distillation is Used to Separate a Mixture of Liquids

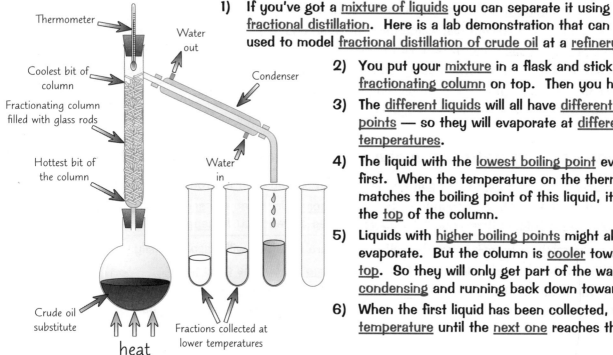

Thermometer

Water out

Coolest bit of column

Condenser

Fractionating column filled with glass rods

Hottest bit of the column

Water in

Crude oil substitute

heat

Fractions collected at lower temperatures

1) If you've got a <u>mixture of liquids</u> you can separate it using <u>fractional distillation</u>. Here is a lab demonstration that can be used to model <u>fractional distillation of crude oil</u> at a <u>refinery</u>.

2) You put your <u>mixture</u> in a flask and stick a <u>fractionating column</u> on top. Then you heat it.

3) The <u>different liquids</u> will all have <u>different boiling points</u> — so they will evaporate at <u>different temperatures</u>.

4) The liquid with the <u>lowest boiling point</u> evaporates first. When the temperature on the thermometer matches the boiling point of this liquid, it will reach the <u>top</u> of the column.

5) Liquids with <u>higher boiling points</u> might also start to evaporate. But the column is <u>cooler</u> towards the <u>top</u>. So they will only get part of the way up before <u>condensing</u> and running back down towards the flask.

6) When the first liquid has been collected, you <u>raise the temperature</u> until the <u>next one</u> reaches the top.

Fractionating — sounds a bit too much like maths to me...

You made it to the end of separation techniques. Congratulations. Now all you need to do is learn these techniques. Shouldn't be too tricky. Make sure you scribble all this stuff down — you'd be crazy not to.

Q1 Propan-1-ol, methanol and ethanol have boiling points of 97 °C, 65 °C and 78 °C respectively. A student uses fractional distillation to separate a mixture of these compounds. State which liquid will be collected in the second fraction and explain why. [2 marks]

The History of The Atom

You might have thought you were done with the atom after page 12. Unfortunately amigo, you don't get away that easily — there's more you need to learn. Hold on to your hat, you're going on a journey through time...

The Theory of Atomic Structure Has Changed Over Time

1) At the start of the 19th century John Dalton described atoms as solid spheres, and said that different spheres made up the different elements.

2) In 1897 J J Thomson concluded from his experiments that atoms weren't solid spheres. His measurements of charge and mass showed that an atom must contain even smaller, negatively charged particles — electrons. The 'solid sphere' idea of atomic structure had to be changed. The new theory was known as the 'plum pudding model'.

3) The plum pudding model showed the atom as a ball of positive charge with electrons stuck in it.

Rutherford Showed that the Plum Pudding Model Was Wrong

1) In 1909 Ernest Rutherford and his student Ernest Marsden conducted the famous alpha particle scattering experiments. They fired positively charged alpha particles at an extremely thin sheet of gold.

2) From the plum pudding model, they were expecting the particles to pass straight through the sheet or be slightly deflected at most. This was because the positive charge of each atom was thought to be very spread out through the 'pudding' of the atom. But, whilst most of the particles did go straight through the gold sheet, some were deflected more than expected, and a small number were deflected backwards. So the plum pudding model couldn't be right.

3) Rutherford came up with an idea to explain this new evidence — the nuclear model of the atom. In this, there's a tiny, positively charged nucleus at the centre, where most of the mass is concentrated. A 'cloud' of negative electrons surrounds this nucleus — so most of the atom is empty space. When alpha particles came near the concentrated, positive charge of the nucleus, they were deflected. If they were fired directly at the nucleus, they were deflected backwards. Otherwise, they passed through the empty space.

Bohr's Nuclear Model Explains a Lot

1) Scientists realised that electrons in a 'cloud' around the nucleus of an atom, as Rutherford described, would be attracted to the nucleus, causing the atom to collapse. Niels Bohr's nuclear model of the atom suggested that all the electrons were contained in shells.

2) Bohr proposed that electrons orbit the nucleus in fixed shells and aren't anywhere in between. Each shell is a fixed distance from the nucleus.

3) Bohr's theory of atomic structure was supported by many experiments and it helped to explain lots of other scientists' observations at the time.

Further Experiments Showed the Existence of Protons

1) Further experiments by Rutherford and others showed that the nucleus can be divided into smaller particles, which each have the same charge as a hydrogen nucleus. These particles were named protons.

2) About 20 years after scientists had accepted that atoms have nuclei, James Chadwick carried out an experiment which provided evidence for neutral particles in the nucleus which are now called neutrons. The discovery of neutrons resulted in a model of the atom which was pretty close to the modern day accepted version, known as the nuclear model (see page 12).

I wanted to be a model — but I ate too much plum pudding...

In science, other people's work is constantly being built upon — increasing our understanding of a topic.

Q1   Describe the 'plum pudding' model of the atom.   [1 mark]

Q2   Rutherford devised an experiment where alpha particles were fired through gold foil. Most of the particles passed through the foil, but some were deflected by different angles, and some were even deflected backwards. Explain why this disproves the plum pudding model.   [2 marks]

Electronic Structure

The fact that electrons occupy 'shells' around the nucleus is what causes the whole of chemistry. Remember that, and watch how it applies to each bit of it. It's ace.

Electron Shell Rules:

1) Electrons always occupy <u>shells</u> (sometimes called <u>energy levels</u>).

2) The <u>lowest</u> energy levels are <u>always filled first</u> — these are the ones closest to the nucleus.

3) Only <u>a certain number</u> of electrons are allowed in each shell:
   <u>1st shell: **2**</u>   <u>2nd shell: **8**</u>   <u>3rd shell: **8**</u>

4) Atoms are much <u>happier</u> when they have <u>full electron shells</u> — like the <u>noble gases</u> in <u>Group 0</u>.

5) In most atoms, the <u>outer shell</u> is <u>not full</u> and this makes the atom want to <u>react</u> to fill it.

Electron configurations can be shown as <u>diagrams</u> like this...

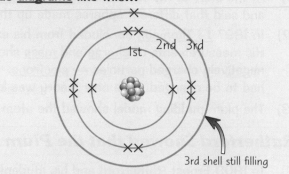

3rd shell still filling

...or as <u>numbers</u> like this: 2, 8, 1

Both of the configurations above are for <u>sodium</u>.

Follow the Rules to Work Out Electronic Structures

You can easily work out the <u>electronic structures</u> for the first <u>20</u> elements of the periodic table (things get a bit more complicated after that).

EXAMPLE: What is the electronic structure of nitrogen?

1) Nitrogen's atomic number is 7. This means it has 7 protons... so it must have 7 electrons.
2) Follow the 'Electron Shell Rules' above. The first shell can only take 2 electrons and the second shell can take a maximum of 8 electrons.

So the electronic structure for nitrogen must be 2, 5.

EXAMPLE: What is the electronic structure of magnesium?

1) Magnesium's atomic number is 12. This means it has 12 protons... so it must have 12 electrons.
2) Follow the 'Electron Shell Rules' above. The first shell can only take 2 electrons and the second shell can take a maximum of 8 electrons, so the third shell must also be partially filled.

So the electronic structure for magnesium must be 2, 8, 2.

Here are some more examples of electronic structures:

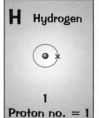

H Hydrogen

1
Proton no. = 1

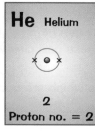

He Helium

2
Proton no. = 2

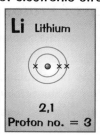

Li Lithium

2,1
Proton no. = 3

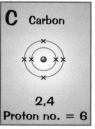

C Carbon

2,4
Proton no. = 6

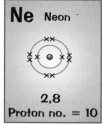

Ne Neon

2,8
Proton no. = 10

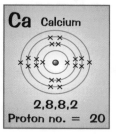

Ca Calcium

2,8,8,2
Proton no. = 20

The electronic structure of the fifth element — it's a bit boron...

Electronic structures may seem a bit complicated at first but once you learn the rules, it's a piece of cake. And just like cake, you'll never regret going back for some more. Better get practising.

Q1   Give the electronic structure of aluminium (atomic number = 13).   [1 mark]

Q2   Give the electronic structure of argon (atomic number = 18).   [1 mark]

Development of the Periodic Table

We haven't always known as much about chemistry as we do now. No sirree. Early chemists looked to try and understand <u>patterns</u> in the elements' properties to get a bit of understanding.

In the Early 1800s Elements Were Arranged By Atomic Mass

Until quite recently, there were <u>two</u> obvious ways to categorise elements:

> 1) Their <u>physical</u> and <u>chemical properties</u>. 2) Their <u>relative atomic mass</u>.

1) Remember, scientists had <u>no idea</u> of <u>atomic structure</u> or of <u>protons</u>, neutrons or <u>electrons</u>, so there was no such thing as <u>atomic number</u> to them. (It was only in the 20th century after protons and electrons were discovered that it was realised the elements were best arranged in order of <u>atomic number</u>.)

Remember — the relative atomic mass is the average mass of one atom of an element.

2) <u>Back then</u>, the only thing they could measure was <u>relative atomic mass</u>, and so the <u>known</u> elements were arranged <u>in order of atomic mass</u>. When this was done, a <u>periodic pattern</u> was noticed in the <u>properties</u> of the elements. This is where the name '<u>periodic table</u>' comes from — ta da...

3) Early periodic tables were not complete and some elements were placed in the <u>wrong group</u>. This is because <u>elements</u> were placed in the <u>order of relative atomic mass</u> and did not take into account their properties.

Dmitri Mendeleev Left Gaps and Predicted New Elements

1) In <u>1869</u>, <u>Dmitri Mendeleev</u> overcame some of the problems of early periodic tables by taking 50 known elements and arranging them into his Table of Elements — with various <u>gaps</u> as shown.

Mendeleev's Table of the Elements

H																	
Li	Be											B	C	N	O	F	
Na	Mg											Al	Si	P	S	Cl	
K	Ca	*	Ti	V	Cr	Mn	Fe	Co	Ni	Cu	Zn	*	*	As	Se	Br	
Rb	Sr	Y	Zr	Nb	Mo	*	Ru	Rh	Pd	Ag	Cd	In	Sn	Sb	Te	I	
Cs	Ba	*	*	Ta	W	*	Os	Ir	Pt	Au	Hg	Tl	Pb	Bi			

2) <u>Mendeleev</u> put the elements <u>mainly</u> in order of <u>atomic mass</u> but did switch that order if the properties meant it should be changed. An example of this can been seen with <u>Te</u> and <u>I</u> — iodine actually has a <u>smaller</u> relative atomic mass but is placed after tellurium as it has <u>similar properties</u> to the elements in that group.

3) <u>Gaps</u> were left in the table to make sure that elements with similar properties stayed in the same groups. Some of these <u>gaps</u> indicated the existence of undiscovered elements and allowed Mendeleev to predict what their properties might be. When they were found and they <u>fitted the pattern</u> it helped confirm Mendeleev's ideas. For example, Mendeleev made really good predictions about the chemical and physical properties of an element he called <u>ekasilicon</u>, which we know today as <u>germanium</u>.

> The discovery of <u>isotopes</u> (see page 13) in the early 20th century confirmed that Mendeleev was correct to <u>not</u> place elements in a <u>strict order</u> of atomic mass but to also take account of their <u>properties</u>. Isotopes of the same element have <u>different atomic masses</u> but have the same <u>chemical properties</u> so occupy the same position on the periodic table.

You should come back to this page periodically...

Ahh more history... This is science at its best, discoveries building upon discoveries — all leading to the point where you have to learn it. Mendeleev would be proud... of himself and you of course.

Q1   How were elements classified in the early 1800s?   [1 mark]

Q2   Describe two changes that Mendeleev made to early periodic tables.   [2 marks]

The Modern Periodic Table

So, as you've seen it took a while to get to the <u>periodic table</u> that you will (soon) know and love. I present to you a chemist's best friend...

The Periodic Table Helps you to See Patterns in Properties

1) There are <u>100ish elements</u>, which all materials are made of.

2) In the periodic table the elements are laid out in order of <u>increasing atomic (proton) number</u>. Arranging the elements like this means there are <u>repeating patterns</u> in the <u>properties</u> of the elements. (The properties are said to occur <u>periodically</u>, hence the name <u>periodic table</u>.)

3) If it wasn't for the periodic table <u>organising everything</u>, you'd have a <u>heck of a job</u> remembering all those properties. It's <u>ace</u>.

4) It's a handy tool for working out which elements are <u>metals</u> and which are <u>non-metals</u>. Metals are found to the <u>left</u> and non-metals to the <u>right</u>.

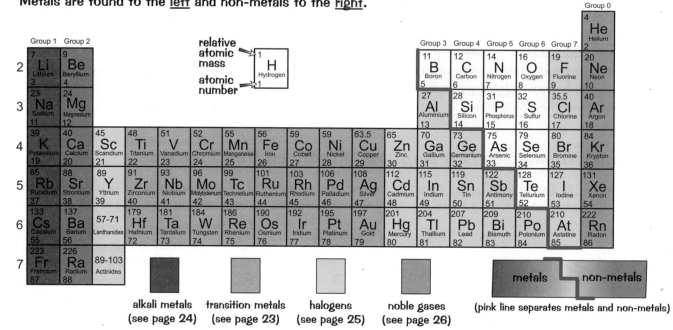

alkali metals (see page 24)   transition metals (see page 23)   halogens (see page 25)   noble gases (see page 26)   (pink line separates metals and non-metals)

5) Elements with <u>similar properties</u> form <u>columns</u>.

6) These <u>vertical columns</u> are called <u>groups</u>.

7) The <u>group number</u> tells you how many <u>electrons</u> there are in the <u>outer shell</u>. For example, <u>Group 1</u> elements all have <u>one</u> electron in their outer shell and <u>Group 7</u> all have <u>seven</u> electrons in their outer shell. The exception to the rule is <u>group 0</u>, for example Helium has two electrons in its outer shell. This is useful as the way atoms react depends upon <u>the number of electrons</u> in their <u>outer shell</u>. So all elements in the same group are likely to react in a similar way.

8) If you know the <u>properties</u> of <u>one element</u>, you can <u>predict</u> properties of <u>other elements</u> in that group — and in the exam, you might be asked to do this. For example the <u>Group 1</u> elements are Li, Na, K, Rb, Cs and Fr. They're all <u>metals</u> and they <u>react in a similar way</u> (see page 24).

9) You can also make predictions about trends in <u>reactivity</u>. E.g. in Group 1, the elements react <u>more vigorously</u> as you go <u>down</u> the group. And in Group 7, <u>reactivity decreases</u> as you go down the group.

10) The <u>rows</u> are called <u>periods</u>. Each new period represents another <u>full shell</u> of electrons.

I'm in a chemistry band — I play the symbols...

Because the periodic table is organised into groups and periods, it allows us to see trends in both reactivity and properties. And this means we can make predictions on how reactions will occur. How neat is that?

Q1   Using a periodic table, state how many electrons beryllium has in its outer shell.   [1 mark]

Q2   Chlorine reacts in a similar way to bromine. Suggest a reason why.   [1 mark]

Q3   Sodium readily forms 1+ ions. Suggest what ions potassium forms and explain why.   [1 mark]

Topic 1 — Atomic Structure and the Periodic Table

Metals and Non-Metals

I can almost guarantee you'll touch something <u>metallic</u> today, that's how important metals are to modern life.

Most Elements are Metals

1) Metals are elements which can <u>form positive ions</u> when they react.
2) They're towards the <u>bottom</u> and to the <u>left</u> of the periodic table.
3) <u>Most elements</u> in the periodic table are metals.
4) <u>Non-metals</u> are at the far <u>right</u> and <u>top</u> of the periodic table.
5) Non-metals <u>don't</u> generally <u>form positive ions</u> when they react.

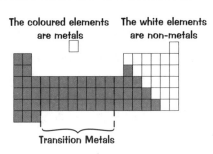
The coloured elements are metals   The white elements are non-metals
Transition Metals

The Electronic Structure of Atoms Affects How They Will React

1) Atoms generally react to form a <u>full outer shell</u>. They do this via <u>losing</u>, <u>gaining</u> or <u>sharing</u> electrons.
2) Metals to the <u>left</u> of the periodic table <u>don't</u> have many <u>electrons to remove</u> and metals towards the <u>bottom</u> of the periodic table have outer electrons which are a <u>long way</u> from the nucleus so feel a weaker attraction. <u>Both</u> these effects means that <u>not much energy</u> is needed to remove the electrons so it's <u>feasible</u> for the elements to react to <u>form positive ions</u> with a full outer shell.
3) For <u>non-metals</u>, forming positive ions is much <u>more difficult</u>. This is as they are either to the right of the periodic table — where they have <u>lots of electrons</u> to remove to get a full outer shell, or towards the top — where the outer electrons are close to the nucleus so feel a <u>strong attraction</u>. It's far more feasible for them to either <u>share</u> or <u>gain</u> electrons to get a full outer shell.

Metals and Non-Metals Have Different Physical Properties

1) All metals have <u>metallic bonding</u> which causes them to have <u>similar</u> basic physical properties.
   - They're <u>strong</u> (hard to break), but can be <u>bent</u> or <u>hammered</u> into different shapes (malleable).
   - They're great at <u>conducting heat</u> and <u>electricity</u>.
   - They have high <u>boiling and melting points</u>.
2) As non-metals <u>don't</u> have metallic bonding, they don't tend to exhibit the same properties as metals. They tend to be <u>dull looking</u>, more <u>brittle</u>, <u>aren't always solids</u> at room temperature, <u>don't</u> generally <u>conduct electricity</u> and often have a <u>lower density</u>.

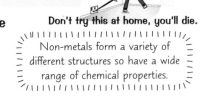
Don't try this at home, you'll die.
Non-metals form a variety of different structures so have a wide range of chemical properties.

Transition Metals can be Found Between Group 2 and Group 3

1) <u>Transition metals</u> are in the <u>centre</u> of the periodic table (see above).
2) Transition metals are <u>typical metals</u>, and have the properties you would expect of a 'proper' metal — they're good <u>conductors</u> of heat and electricity, and they're very <u>dense</u>, <u>strong</u> and <u>shiny</u>.
3) Transition metals also have some pretty <u>special</u> properties...
   - Transition metals can have <u>more than one</u> ion. For example, copper forms Cu^+ and Cu^{2+} ions. Cobalt forms Co^{2+} and Co^{3+} ions.
   - Transition metal ions are often <u>coloured</u>, and so <u>compounds</u> that contain them are <u>colourful</u>. For example, potassium chromate(VI), which is yellow, potassium(VII) manganate is <u>purple</u>.
   - Transition metal compounds often make good <u>catalysts</u> (things that speed up the rate of a reaction — see p.68). For example, a <u>nickel</u> based catalyst is used in the hydrogenation of alkenes (p.79), and an <u>iron</u> catalyst is used in the <u>Haber process</u> for making ammonia (p.104).

You can 'rock out' to metal, you can sway gently to non-metal...

Metals and non-metals are like chalk and cheese... Though I hope there's no metal in your cheese.

Q1   State three properties of metals.   [3 marks]

Group 1 Elements

Group 1 elements are known as the <u>alkali metals</u>. As metals go, they're pretty <u>reactive</u>.

The Group 1 Elements are Reactive, Soft Metals

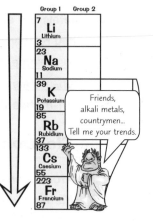

1) The alkali metals are lithium, sodium, potassium, rubidium, caesium and francium.
2) They all have <u>one electron</u> in their outer shell which makes them <u>very reactive</u> and gives them <u>similar properties</u>.
3) The alkali metals are all <u>soft</u> and have <u>low density</u>.
4) The <u>trends</u> for the alkali metals as you go <u>down</u> Group 1 include:

- <u>Increasing reactivity</u> — the outer electron is <u>more easily lost</u> as the attraction between the nucleus and electron decreases, because the electron is <u>further away</u> from the nucleus the further down the group you go.
- <u>Lower melting</u> and <u>boiling</u> points.
- <u>Higher relative atomic mass</u>.

Alkali Metals Form Ionic Compounds with Non-Metals

Don't worry, there's more on ionic compounds on page 30.

1) The Group 1 elements don't need much energy to lose their one outer electron to form a full outer shell, so they readily form <u>1+ ions</u>.
2) It's so easy for them to lose their outer electron that they only ever react to form <u>ionic compounds</u>. These compounds are generally <u>white solids</u> that dissolve in water to form <u>colourless solutions</u>.

Reaction with water

- When Group 1 metals are put in <u>water</u>, they react <u>vigorously</u> to produce <u>hydrogen gas</u> and <u>metal hydroxides</u> — salts that dissolve in water to produce <u>alkaline solutions</u>.

$$2Na_{(s)} + 2H_2O_{(l)} \rightarrow 2NaOH_{(aq)} + H_{2(g)}$$
sodium + water → sodium hydroxide + hydrogen

- The <u>more reactive</u> (lower down in the group) an alkali metal is, the more violent the reaction.
- The amount of <u>energy</u> given out by the reaction increases down the group — the reaction with potassium releases enough energy to ignite hydrogen.

All the Group 1 metals react with water in a similar way.

Reaction with chlorine

1) Group 1 metals react <u>vigorously</u> when heated in <u>chlorine gas</u> to form white <u>metal chloride salts</u>.

$$2Na_{(s)} + Cl_{2(g)} \rightarrow 2NaCl_{(s)}$$
sodium + chlorine → sodium chloride

2) As you go down the group, reactivity increases so the reaction with chlorine gets <u>more vigorous</u>.

Reaction with oxygen

The Group 1 metals can react with <u>oxygen</u> to form a <u>metal oxide</u>. Different types of <u>oxide</u> will form depending on the Group 1 metal:

The reactions with oxygen are why Group 1 metals tarnish in the air — the metal reacts with oxygen in the air to form a dull metal oxide layer.

- Lithium reacts to form <u>lithium oxide</u> (Li_2O).
- Sodium reacts to form a mixture of <u>sodium oxide</u> (Na_2O) and <u>sodium peroxide</u> (Na_2O_2).
- Potassium reacts to form a mixture of <u>potassium peroxide</u> (K_2O_2) and <u>potassium superoxide</u> (KO_2).

Group 1 Metals Have Different Properties to Transition Metals

1) Group 1 metals are much <u>more reactive</u> than transition metals — they react more vigorously with <u>water</u>, <u>oxygen</u> or <u>Group 7 elements</u>, for example.
2) They're also much less <u>dense</u>, <u>strong</u> and <u>hard</u> than the transition metals, and have much <u>lower melting points</u>. E.g. manganese melts at 2000 °C, sodium melts at 98 °C.

Back to the drawing board with my lithium swim shorts design...

Reactions of alkali metals need safety precautions, but they fizz in water and might explode. Cool.

Q1 Explain the trend in reactivity as you go down Group 1. [2 marks]

Group 7 Elements

The Group 7 elements are known as the halogens. The whole 'trend thing' happens with the halogens as well — that shouldn't come as a surprise.

The Halogens are All Non-Metals with Coloured Vapours

Fluorine is a very reactive, poisonous yellow gas.

Chlorine is a fairly reactive, poisonous dense green gas.

Bromine is a dense, poisonous, red-brown volatile liquid.

Iodine is a dark grey crystalline solid or a purple vapour.

They all exist as molecules which are pairs of atoms.

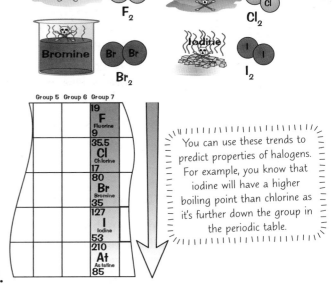

Learn These Trends:

As you go DOWN Group 7, the halogens:

1) become LESS REACTIVE — it's harder to gain an extra electron, because the outer shell's further from the nucleus.

2) have HIGHER MELTING AND BOILING POINTS.

3) have HIGHER RELATIVE ATOMIC MASSES.

All the Group 7 elements react in similar ways. This is because they all have seven electrons in their outer shell.

You can use these trends to predict properties of halogens. For example, you know that iodine will have a higher boiling point than chlorine as it's further down the group in the periodic table.

Halogens can Form Molecular Compounds

Halogen atoms can share electrons via covalent bonding (see page 31) with other non-metals so as to achieve a full outer shell. For example HCl, PCl_5, HF and CCl_4 contain covalent bonds. The compounds that form when halogens react with non-metals all have simple molecular structures (see p.32).

Halogens Form Ionic Bonds with Metals

1) The halogens form 1– ions called halides (F^-, Cl^-, Br^- and I^-) when they bond with metals, for example Na^+Cl^- or $Fe^{3+}Br^-_3$.

2) The compounds that form have ionic structures.

3) The diagram shows the bonding in sodium chloride, NaCl.

More Reactive Halogens Will Displace Less Reactive Ones

A displacement reaction can occur between a more reactive halogen and the salt of a less reactive one.

E.g. chlorine can displace bromine and iodine from an aqueous solution of its salt (a bromide or iodide). Bromine will also displace iodine because of the trend in reactivity.

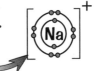

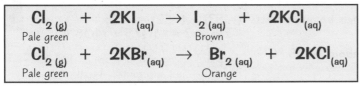

$$Cl_{2\,(g)} + 2KI_{(aq)} \rightarrow I_{2\,(aq)} + 2KCl_{(aq)}$$
Pale green   Brown

$$Cl_{2\,(g)} + 2KBr_{(aq)} \rightarrow Br_{2\,(aq)} + 2KCl_{(aq)}$$
Pale green   Orange

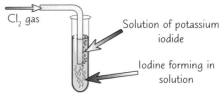

Cl_2 gas

Solution of potassium iodide

Iodine forming in solution

I can see your halo(gen), halo(gen) halo(gen)...

You say 'halo-gen' I say 'ha-logen', lets call the whole thing off... Apart from revision, let's call that whole thing 'on'. Displacement reactions are pretty important in chemistry — better learn the facts.

Q1   Predict whether bromine would displace iodine from sodium iodide and explain why.   [2 marks]

Q2   Why do Group 7 elements get less reactive as you go down the group from fluorine to iodine?   [3 marks]

Group 0 Elements

The Group 0 elements are known as <u>noble gases</u> — stuffed full of every honourable virtue.
They don't react with very much and you can't even see them — making them, well, a bit dull really.

Group 0 Elements are All Inert, Colourless Gases

1) Group 0 elements are called the <u>noble gases</u> and include the elements <u>helium</u>, <u>neon</u> and <u>argon</u> (plus a few others).

2) They all have <u>eight electrons</u> in their outer energy level, apart from helium which has two, giving them a <u>full outer-shell</u>. As their outer shell is energetically stable they don't need to <u>give up</u> or <u>gain</u> electrons to become more stable. This means they are more or less <u>inert</u> — they <u>don't react</u> with much at all.

Helium only has electrons in the first shell, which only needs 2 to be filled.

3) They exist as <u>monatomic gases</u> — single atoms <u>not</u> bonded to each other.

4) All elements in Group 0 are <u>colourless gases</u> at room temperature.

5) As the noble gases are inert they're <u>non-flammable</u> — they won't set on fire.

There are Patterns in the Properties of the Noble Gases

1) The <u>boiling points</u> of the noble gases <u>increase</u> as you move <u>down</u> the group along with increasing relative atomic mass.

Noble Gas
helium
neon
argon
krypton
xenon
radon

Increasing boiling point

2) The increase in boiling point is due to an <u>increase</u> in the <u>number of electrons</u> in each <u>atom</u> leading to <u>greater intermolecular forces</u> between them which need to be overcome. There's more on intermolecular forces for small molecules on page 32.

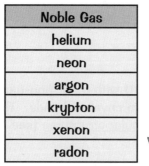

Here's another pattern. You don't have to learn this one...

3) In the exam you may be given the boiling point of one noble gas and asked to <u>estimate</u> the value for <u>another one</u>. So make sure you know the <u>pattern</u>.

EXAMPLE: Neon is a gas at 25 °C. Predict what state helium is at this temperature.

Helium has a lower boiling point than neon as it is further up the group.

So, helium must also be a gas at 25 °C.

EXAMPLE: Radon and krypton have boiling points of −62 °C and −153 °C respectively. Predict the boiling point of xenon.

Xenon comes in between radon and krypton in the group so you can predict that its boiling point would be halfway between their boiling points: $(-153) + (-62) = -215$
$-215 \div 2 = -107.5 \approx -108°C$

So, xenon should have a boiling point of about −108 °C

The actual boiling point of xenon is −108 °C — just as predicted. Neat!

...or this one.

Arrrgon — the pirate element...

As noble gases don't really react there isn't too much to learn about them. If you understand why they are unreactive and the trend in boiling points as you go down the group you're sorted.

Q1   Does xenon or neon have the higher boiling point?   [1 mark]

Q2   Argon is very unreactive. Using your knowledge of its electronic structure, explain why.   [2 marks]

Revision Questions for Topic 1

Well, that wraps up Topic 1 — time to put yourself to the test and find out how much you really know.

- Try these questions and tick off each one when you get it right.
- When you've done all the questions under a heading and are completely happy with it, tick it off.

Atoms, Elements and Compounds (p.12-15) ☐

1) Sketch an atom. Label the nucleus and the electrons.
2) What is the charge of a proton? $+1$
3) True or False? Elements contain more than one type of atom. *(False circled)*
4) Give the formula for:
   a) Carbon dioxide   b) Sodium carbonate   (a) CO_2 (b) $NaCO$
5) Balance these equations:
   a) $Mg_1 + O_2 \rightarrow 2MgO$ b) $H_2SO_4 + 2NaOH \rightarrow Na_2SO_4 + 2H_2O$

Mixtures and Separation (p.16-18) ☐

6) What is the difference between a compound and a mixture?
7) What is the name of the pattern formed from carrying out paper chromatography? Chromatogram
8) Which method of separation is useful to separate an insoluble solid from a liquid? Cristallisation
9) Give the name of a method to separate a soluble solid from a liquid. evaporation
10) Which method of distillation would you use to separate liquids with similar boiling points? distillation

Electronic Structure and the History of the Periodic Table (p.19-22) ☐

11) Who discovered that the plum pudding model was wrong? JJ Thompson
12) Who first devised an experiment that proved the existence of the neutron?
13) What is the electronic structure of sodium? 2, 8, 1
14) Why did Mendeleev leave gaps in his Table of Elements? undiscovered elements

Groups of the Periodic Table (p.23-26) ☐

15) How are the group number and the number of electrons in the outer shell of an element related? same number
16) What kind of ions do metals form? positive ions
17) Where are non-metals on the periodic table? by the right of the periodic table
18) Give three properties which are specific to transition metals. coloured, dense, strong ishiny
19) State three trends as you go down Group 1. becomes more reactive, lower melting & bp, higher relative atomic mass
20) State the products of the reaction of sodium and water. Produce hydrogen gas
21) State the differences between Group 1 and transition metals for the following properties:
   a) Hardness   b) Reactivity *(circled)*   c) Melting Points
22) How do the boiling points of halogens change as you go down the group from fluorine to astatine? increasing
23) What is the charge of the ions that halogens form when they react with metals? -1
24) Predict whether iodine is displaced by chlorine in a solution of potassium iodide.
25) What is the trend in boiling point as you go down Group 0? increases

Formation of Ions

Ions crop up all over the place in chemistry. You're gonna have to be able to explain <u>how</u> they form and predict the <u>charges</u> of simple ions formed by elements in Groups 1, 2, 6 and 7. You'd better get on...

Ions are Made When Electrons are Transferred

1) <u>Ions</u> are <u>charged</u> particles — they can be <u>single atoms</u> (e.g. Cl^-) or <u>groups of atoms</u> (e.g. NO_3^-).

2) When <u>atoms</u> lose or gain electrons to form ions, all they're trying to do is get a <u>full outer shell</u> like a <u>noble gas</u> (also called a "<u>stable electronic structure</u>"). Atoms with full outer shells are very <u>stable</u>.

> Remember that the noble gases are in Group 0 of the periodic table.

3) When <u>metals</u> form ions, they <u>lose</u> electrons from their <u>outer shell</u> to form <u>positive ions</u>.

4) When <u>non-metals</u> form ions, they <u>gain</u> electrons into their <u>outer shell</u> to form <u>negative ions</u>.

5) The <u>number</u> of electrons lost or gained is the same as the <u>charge</u> on the ion. E.g. If 2 electrons are <u>lost</u> the charge is 2+. If 3 electrons are <u>gained</u> the charge is 3−.

Groups 1 & 2 and 6 & 7 are the Most Likely to Form Ions

1) The elements that most readily form ions are those in Groups 1, 2, 6 and 7.

2) <u>Group 1 and 2 elements</u> are <u>metals</u> and they <u>lose</u> electrons to form <u>positive ions</u> (<u>cations</u>).

3) <u>Group 6 and 7 elements</u> are <u>non-metals</u>. They <u>gain</u> electrons to form <u>negative ions</u> (<u>anions</u>).

4) You <u>don't</u> have to <u>remember</u> what ions <u>most elements</u> form — nope, you just look at the periodic table.

5) Elements in the same <u>group</u> all have the same number of <u>outer electrons</u>. So they have to <u>lose or gain</u> the same number to get a full outer shell. And this means that they form ions with the <u>same charges</u>.

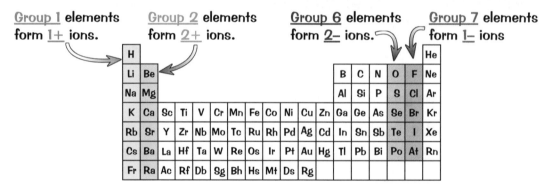

Group 1 elements form 1+ ions.   Group 2 elements form 2+ ions.   Group 6 elements form 2− ions.   Group 7 elements form 1− ions

- A <u>sodium</u> atom (Na) is in <u>Group 1</u> so it <u>loses</u> 1 electron to form a sodium ion (Na^+) with the same electronic structure as <u>neon</u>: $Na \rightarrow Na^+ + e^-$.

- A <u>magnesium</u> atom (Mg) is in <u>Group 2</u> so it <u>loses</u> 2 electrons to form a magnesium ion (Mg^{2+}) with the same electronic structure as <u>neon</u>: $Mg \rightarrow Mg^{2+} + 2e^-$.

- A <u>chlorine</u> atom (Cl) is in <u>Group 7</u> so it <u>gains</u> 1 electron to form a chloride ion (Cl^-) with the same electronic structure as <u>argon</u>: $Cl + e^- \rightarrow Cl^-$.

- An <u>oxygen</u> atom (O) is in <u>Group 6</u> so it <u>gains</u> 2 electrons to form an oxide ion (O^{2-}) with the same electronic structure as <u>neon</u>: $O + 2e^- \rightarrow O^{2-}$.

Dougal was a few electrons short of a full shell.

> Have a look back at page 20 for how to work out electronic structures.

I've got my ion you...

Some elements like to gain electrons, some elements like to lose electrons, but they all want to have a full outer shell. Poor little electron shells, all they want in life is to be full...

Q1   Explain why simple ions often have noble gas electronic structures.   [2 marks]

Q2   Predict the charges of the ions formed by the following elements:
       a) Bromine (Br)   b) Calcium (Ca)   c) Potassium (K)   [3 marks]

Ionic Bonding

Time to find out how particles bond together to form compounds (bet you can't wait). There are <u>three</u> types of bonding you need to know about — <u>ionic</u>, <u>covalent</u> and <u>metallic</u>. First up, it's <u>ionic bonds</u>.

Ionic Bonding — Transfer of Electrons

When a <u>metal</u> and a <u>non-metal</u> react together, the <u>metal atom loses</u> electrons to form a <u>positively charged ion</u> and the <u>non-metal gains these electrons</u> to form a <u>negatively charged ion</u>. These oppositely charged ions are <u>strongly attracted</u> to one another by <u>electrostatic forces</u>. This attraction is called an <u>ionic bond</u>.

Dot and Cross Diagrams Show How Ionic Compounds are Formed

<u>Dot and cross diagrams</u> show the <u>arrangement</u> of electrons in an atom or ion. Each electron is represented by a <u>dot</u> or a <u>cross</u>. So these diagrams can show which <u>atom</u> the electrons in an <u>ion</u> originally came from.

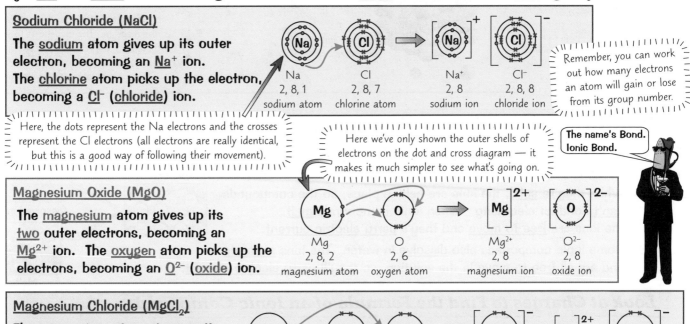

Sodium Chloride (NaCl)

The <u>sodium</u> atom gives up its outer electron, becoming an Na^+ ion.
The <u>chlorine</u> atom picks up the electron, becoming a Cl^- (chloride) ion.

Here, the dots represent the Na electrons and the crosses represent the Cl electrons (all electrons are really identical, but this is a good way of following their movement).

Remember, you can work out how many electrons an atom will gain or lose from its group number.

Here we've only shown the outer shells of electrons on the dot and cross diagram — it makes it much simpler to see what's going on.

The name's Bond. Ionic Bond.

Magnesium Oxide (MgO)

The <u>magnesium</u> atom gives up its <u>two</u> outer electrons, becoming an Mg^{2+} ion. The <u>oxygen</u> atom picks up the electrons, becoming an O^{2-} (oxide) ion.

Magnesium Chloride (MgCl$_2$)

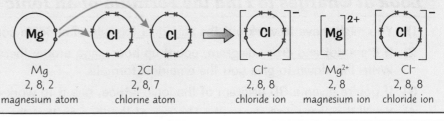

The <u>magnesium</u> atom gives up its <u>two</u> outer electrons, becoming an Mg^{2+} ion. The two <u>chlorine</u> atoms pick up <u>one electron each</u>, becoming <u>two Cl$^-$</u> (chloride) ions.

Sodium Oxide (Na$_2$O)

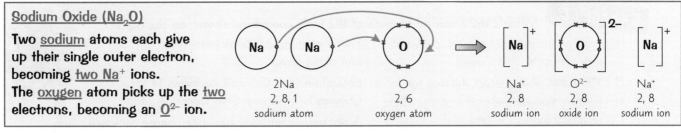

Two <u>sodium</u> atoms each give up their single outer electron, becoming <u>two Na$^+$</u> ions.
The <u>oxygen</u> atom picks up the <u>two</u> electrons, becoming an O^{2-} ion.

Dot and cross diagrams are useful for showing how ionic compounds are formed, but they <u>don't</u> show the <u>structure</u> of the compound, the <u>size</u> of the ions or how they're <u>arranged</u>. But hey-ho — nothing's perfect.

Any old ion, any old ion — any, any, any old ion...

You need to be able to describe how ionic compounds are formed using both words and dot and cross diagrams. It gets easier with practice, so here are some questions to get you started.

Q1   Describe, in terms of electron transfer, how sodium (Na) and chlorine (Cl)
      react to form sodium chloride (NaCl).   [3 marks]

Q2   Draw a dot and cross diagram to show how potassium (a Group 1 metal) and bromine
      (a Group 7 non metal) form potassium bromide (KBr).   [3 marks]

Ionic Compounds

I'd take everything on this page with a pinch of <u>salt</u> if I were you... Ho ho ho — I jest, it's important really.

Ionic Compounds Have A Regular Lattice Structure

1) <u>Ionic compounds</u> have a structure called a <u>giant ionic lattice</u>.

2) The ions form a closely packed <u>regular lattice</u> arrangement and there are very strong <u>electrostatic forces of attraction</u> between <u>oppositely charged</u> ions, in <u>all directions</u> in the lattice.

The electrostatic attraction between the oppositely charged ions is ionic bonding.

A single crystal of <u>sodium chloride</u> (table salt) is <u>one giant ionic lattice</u>. The Na^+ and Cl^- ions are held together in a regular lattice. The lattice can be represented in different ways...

This model shows the relative sizes of the ions, as well as the regular pattern of an ionic crystal, but it only lets you see the outer layer of the compound.

Make sure you learn what the structure of sodium chloride looks like.

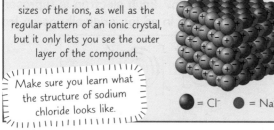

● = Cl^- ● = Na^+

The Na^+ and Cl^- ions alternate.

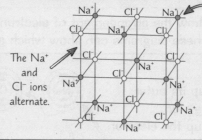

This is a ball and stick model. It shows the regular pattern of an ionic crystal and shows how all the ions are arranged. It also suggests that the crystal extends beyond what's shown in the diagram. The model isn't to scale though, so the relative sizes of the ions may not be shown. Also, in reality, there aren't gaps between the ions.

Ionic Compounds All Have Similar Properties

1) They all have <u>high melting points</u> and <u>high boiling points</u> due to the <u>many strong bonds</u> between the ions. It takes lots of <u>energy</u> to overcome this attraction.

2) When they're <u>solid</u>, the ions are held in place, so the compounds <u>can't</u> conduct electricity. When ionic compounds <u>melt</u>, the ions are <u>free to move</u> and they'll <u>carry electric current</u>.

3) Some ionic compounds also <u>dissolve</u> in water. The ions <u>separate</u> and are all <u>free to move</u> in the solution, so they'll <u>carry electric current</u>.

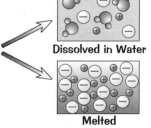

Dissolved in Water

Melted

Look at Charges to Find the Formula of an Ionic Compound

1) You might have to work out the <u>empirical formula</u> of an ionic compound from a diagram of the compound.

2) If it's a <u>dot and cross</u> diagram, count up how <u>many</u> atoms there are of <u>each element</u>. Write this down to give you the empirical formula.

3) If you're given a 3D diagram of the ionic lattice, <u>use</u> it to work out <u>what ions</u> are in the ionic compound.

4) You'll then have to <u>balance</u> the charges of the ions so that the overall charge on the compound is zero.

EXAMPLE: What's the empirical formula of the ionic compound shown on the right?

1) Look at the diagram to work out what ions are in the compound.

2) Work out what <u>charges</u> the ions will form.

3) <u>Balance</u> the charges so the charge of the empirical formula is <u>zero</u>.

The compound contains potassium and oxide ions.

Potassium is in Group 1 so forms 1+ ions. Oxygen is in Group 6 so forms 2− ions.

A potassium ion only has a 1+ charge, so you'll need two of them to balance out the 2− charge of an oxide ion. The empirical formula is K_2O.

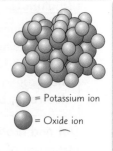

○ = Potassium ion

● = Oxide ion

Giant ionic lattices — all over your chips...

Here's where you can get a little practice working out formulas for ionic compounds.

Q1 The structure of an ionic compound is shown on the right.
  a) Predict, with reasoning, whether the compound
     has a high or a low melting point. [2 marks]
  b) Explain why the compound can conduct electricity when molten. [1 mark]
  c) Use the diagram to find the empirical formula of the compound. [3 marks]

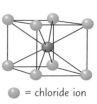

● = chloride ion

● = caesium ion

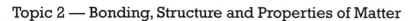

Covalent Bonding

Some elements bond ionically (see page 29) but others form strong <u>covalent</u> bonds.
This is where atoms <u>share</u> electrons with each other so that they've got full outer shells.

Covalent Bonds — Sharing Electrons

1) When <u>non-metal</u> atoms bond together, they <u>share</u> pairs of electrons to make <u>covalent bonds</u>.

2) The positively charged nuclei of the bonded atoms are attracted to the shared pair of electrons by <u>electrostatic forces</u>, making covalent bonds very <u>strong</u>.

3) Atoms only share electrons in their <u>outer shells</u> (highest energy levels).

4) Each single <u>covalent bond</u> provides one <u>extra</u> shared electron for each atom.

5) Each atom involved generally makes <u>enough</u> covalent bonds to <u>fill up</u> its outer shell. Having a full outer shell gives them the electronic structure of a <u>noble gas</u>, which is very <u>stable</u>.

6) Covalent bonding happens in <u>compounds</u> of <u>non-metals</u> (e.g. H_2O) and in <u>non-metal elements</u> (e.g. Cl_2).

There are Different Ways of Drawing Covalent Bonds

1) You can use <u>dot and cross diagrams</u> to show the bonding in covalent compounds.

2) Electrons drawn in the <u>overlap</u> between the outer orbitals of two atoms are <u>shared</u> between those atoms.

3) Dot and cross diagrams are useful for showing <u>which atoms</u> the electrons in a covalent bond come from, but they <u>don't</u> show the relative sizes of the atoms, or how the atoms are <u>arranged</u> in space.

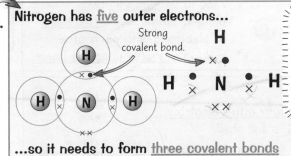

Nitrogen has <u>five</u> outer electrons...
Strong covalent bond.

...so it needs to form <u>three covalent bonds</u> to make up the extra <u>three</u> electrons needed.

You don't have to draw the orbitals in these diagrams. The important thing is that you get all the dots and crosses in the right places.

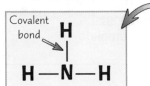
Covalent bond

4) The <u>displayed formula</u> of ammonia (NH_3) shows the covalent bonds as single lines between atoms.

5) This is a great way of showing <u>how</u> atoms are connected in <u>large</u> molecules. However, they <u>don't</u> show the <u>3D structure</u> of the molecule, or <u>which atoms</u> the electrons in the covalent bond have come from.

6) The 3D model of ammonia shows the <u>atoms</u>, the <u>covalent bonds</u> and their <u>arrangement</u> in space next to each other. But 3D models can quickly get <u>confusing</u> for large molecules where there are lots of atoms to include. They don't show <u>where</u> the electrons in the bonds have <u>come from</u>, either.

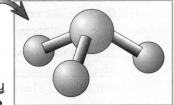

7) You can find the <u>molecular formula</u> of a simple molecular compound from <u>any</u> of these diagrams by <u>counting up</u> how many atoms of each element there are.

A molecular formula shows you how many atoms of each element are in a molecule.

 **EXAMPLE:** A diagram of the molecule ethane is shown on the right. Use the diagram to find the molecular formula of ethane.

In the diagram, there are two carbon atoms and six hydrogen atoms. So the molecular formula is C_2H_6.

Sharing is caring...

There's a whole page of dot and cross diagrams for other covalent molecules yet to come, but make sure you can draw the different diagrams that can be used to show the bonding in ammonia on this page first.

Q1   Draw a dot and cross diagram to show the bonding in a molecule of ammonia (NH_3).   [2 marks]

Simple Molecular Substances

These molecules might be <u>simple</u>, but you've still gotta know about them. I know, the world is a cruel place.

Learn These Examples of Simple Molecular Substances

<u>Simple molecular substances</u> are made up of molecules containing a <u>few atoms</u> joined together by <u>covalent bonds</u>. Here are some <u>common examples</u> that you should know...

<u>Hydrogen, H_2</u>

Hydrogen atoms have just one electron. They <u>only</u> <u>need one more</u> to complete the first shell...

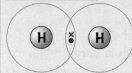

...so they often form <u>single</u> <u>covalent bonds</u>, either with other hydrogen atoms or with other elements, to achieve this.

<u>Oxygen, O_2</u>

Each oxygen atom needs <u>two more electrons</u> to complete its outer shell...

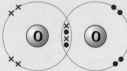

...so in <u>oxygen gas</u> two oxygen atoms share <u>two pairs</u> of electrons with each other making a <u>double covalent bond</u>.

<u>Methane, CH_4</u>

Carbon has <u>four outer electrons</u>, which is <u>half</u> a full shell.

It can form <u>four covalent bonds</u> with <u>hydrogen</u> atoms to fill up its outer shell.

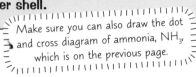

Make sure you can also draw the dot and cross diagram of ammonia, NH_3, which is on the previous page.

<u>Chlorine, Cl_2</u>

Each chlorine atom needs just <u>one more</u> <u>electron</u> to complete the outer shell...

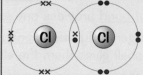

...so two chlorine atoms can share one pair of electrons and form <u>a single covalent bond</u>.

<u>Nitrogen, N_2</u>

Nitrogen atoms need <u>three more</u> electrons...

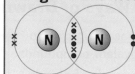

...so <u>two nitrogen atoms</u> share <u>three pairs of electrons</u> to fill their outer shells. This creates a <u>triple bond</u>.

<u>Water, H_2O</u>

In <u>water molecules</u>, the oxygen shares a pair of electrons with two H atoms to form two <u>single covalent bonds</u>.

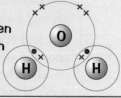

<u>Hydrogen Chloride, HCl</u>

This is very similar to H_2 and Cl_2. Again, both atoms <u>only need</u> <u>one more electron</u> to complete their outer shells.

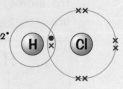

Properties of Simple Molecular Substances

1) Substances containing <u>covalent bonds</u> usually have <u>simple molecular structures</u>, like the examples above.

2) The atoms within the molecules are held together by <u>very strong covalent bonds</u>. By contrast, the forces of attraction <u>between</u> these molecules are <u>very weak</u>.

3) To melt or boil a simple molecular compound, you only need to break these <u>feeble intermolecular forces</u> and <u>not</u> the covalent bonds. So the melting and boiling points are <u>very low</u>, because the molecules are <u>easily parted</u> from each other.

4) Most molecular substances are <u>gases or liquids</u> at room temperature.

5) As molecules get <u>bigger</u>, the strength of the intermolecular forces <u>increases</u>, so <u>more energy</u> is needed to break them, and the melting and boiling points <u>increase</u>.

6) Molecular compounds <u>don't conduct electricity</u>, simply because they <u>aren't charged</u>, so there are <u>no free electrons</u> or ions.

Weak intermolecular forces

Chlorine

Oxygen

May the intermolecular force be with you...

Never forget that it's the weak forces between molecules that are broken when a simple molecular substance melts.

Q1 Explain why oxygen, O_2, is a gas at room temperature. [1 mark]

Q2 Explain why nitrogen, N_2, doesn't conduct electricity. [1 mark]

Polymers and Giant Covalent Structures

Wouldn't it be simply marvellous if only simple molecular substances had covalent bonds, and it was now time to put your feet up? Well it's not like that. <u>Polymers</u> and <u>giant covalent substances</u> also have <u>covalent bonds</u>.

Polymers Are Long Chains of Repeating Units

1) In a polymer, lots of <u>small units</u> are linked together to form a <u>long molecule</u> that has repeating sections.

2) All the atoms in a polymer are joined by strong <u>covalent bonds</u>.

3) Instead of drawing out a whole long polymer molecule (which can contain thousands or even millions of atoms), you can draw the <u>shortest</u> repeating section, called the <u>repeating unit</u>, like this:

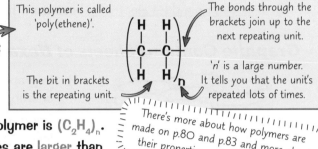

This polymer is called 'poly(ethene)'.

The bonds through the brackets join up to the next repeating unit.

The bit in brackets is the repeating unit.

'*n*' is a large number. It tells you that the unit's repeated lots of times.

4) To find the <u>molecular formula</u> of a polymer, write down the molecular formula of the <u>repeating unit</u> in <u>brackets</u>, and put an '<u>n</u>' outside.

5) So for <u>poly(ethene)</u>, the molecular formula of the polymer is $(C_2H_4)_n$.

6) The intermolecular forces between polymer molecules are <u>larger</u> than between simple covalent molecules, so <u>more energy</u> is needed to break them. This means most polymers are <u>solid</u> at room temperature.

There's more about how polymers are made on p.80 and p.83 and more about their properties and uses on p.96-97.

7) The intermolecular forces are still <u>weaker</u> than ionic or covalent bonds, so they generally have <u>lower</u> boiling points than <u>ionic</u> or <u>giant molecular</u> compounds.

Giant Covalent Structures Are Macromolecules

1) In giant covalent structures, <u>all</u> the atoms are <u>bonded</u> to <u>each other</u> by <u>strong</u> covalent bonds.

2) They have <u>very high</u> melting and boiling points as lots of energy is needed to break the covalent bonds between the atoms.

3) They <u>don't</u> contain charged particles, so they <u>don't conduct electricity</u> — not even when <u>molten</u> (except for a few weird exceptions such as graphite, see next page).

4) The <u>main examples</u> that you need to know about are <u>diamond</u> and <u>graphite</u>, which are both made from <u>carbon atoms</u> only, and <u>silicon dioxide</u> (silica).

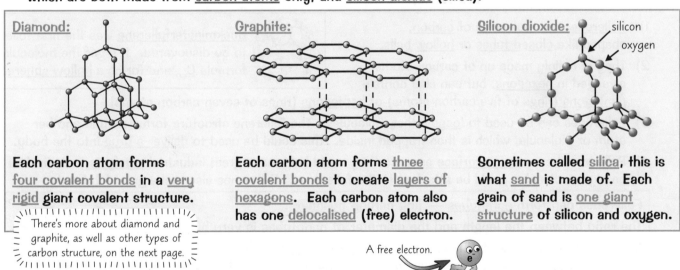

Diamond:

Each carbon atom forms <u>four covalent bonds</u> in a <u>very rigid</u> giant covalent structure.

There's more about diamond and graphite, as well as other types of carbon structure, on the next page.

Graphite:

Each carbon atom forms <u>three covalent bonds</u> to create <u>layers of hexagons</u>. Each carbon atom also has one <u>delocalised</u> (free) electron.

Silicon dioxide:

silicon

oxygen

Sometimes called <u>silica</u>, this is what <u>sand</u> is made of. Each grain of sand is <u>one giant structure</u> of silicon and oxygen.

A free electron.

What do you call a vehicle made of sand? Sili-car...

To melt or boil a simple molecular substance or a polymer, only the weakish intermolecular forces need to be broken. To melt or boil a giant covalent substance, you have to break very strong covalent bonds.

Q1 The repeating unit of poly(chloroethene) is shown on the right. What's the molecular formula of poly(chloroethene)? [1 mark]

Q2 Predict, with reasoning, whether diamond or poly(ethene) has a higher melting point. [3 marks]

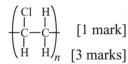

Allotropes of Carbon

Allotropes are different structural forms of the same element in the same physical state. Carbon's got lots...

Diamond is Very Hard

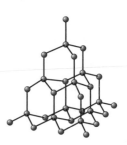

1) Diamond has a giant covalent structure, made up of carbon atoms that each form four covalent bonds. This makes diamond really hard.

2) Those strong covalent bonds take a lot of energy to break and give diamond a very high melting point.

3) It doesn't conduct electricity because it has no free electrons or ions.

Graphite Contains Sheets of Hexagons

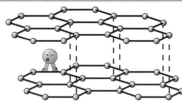

1) In graphite, each carbon atom only forms three covalent bonds, creating sheets of carbon atoms arranged in hexagons.

2) There aren't any covalent bonds between the layers — they're only held together weakly, so they're free to move over each other. This makes graphite soft and slippery, so it's ideal as a lubricating material.

3) Graphite's got a high melting point — the covalent bonds in the layers need loads of energy to break.

4) Only three out of each carbon's four outer electrons are used in bonds, so each carbon atom has one electron that's delocalised (free) and can move. So graphite conducts electricity and thermal energy.

Graphene is One Layer of Graphite

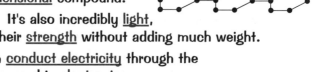

Graphene is a sheet of carbon atoms joined together in hexagons. The sheet is just one atom thick, making it a two-dimensional compound.

The network of covalent bonds makes it very strong. It's also incredibly light, so can be added to composite materials to improve their strength without adding much weight.

Like graphite, it contains delocalised electrons so can conduct electricity through the whole structure. This means it has the potential to be used in electronics.

Fullerenes Form Spheres and Tubes

1) Fullerenes are molecules of carbon, shaped like closed tubes or hollow balls.

Buckminsterfullerene was the first fullerene to be discovered. It's got the molecular formula C_{60} and forms a hollow sphere.

2) They're mainly made up of carbon atoms arranged in hexagons, but can also contain pentagons (rings of five carbon atoms) or heptagons (rings of seven carbon atoms).

3) Fullerenes can be used to 'cage' other molecules. The fullerene structure forms around another atom or molecule, which is then trapped inside. This could be used to deliver a drug into the body.

4) Fullerenes have a huge surface area, so they could help make great industrial catalysts — individual catalyst molecules could be attached to the fullerenes. Fullerenes also make great lubricants.

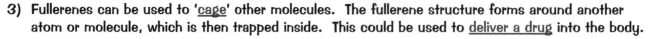

Fullerenes can form nanotubes — tiny carbon cylinders.
The ratio between the length and the diameter of nanotubes is very high.
Nanotubes can conduct both electricity and thermal energy (heat).
They also have a high tensile strength (they don't break when they're stretched).
Technology that uses very small particles such as nanotubes is called nanotechnology. Nanotubes can be used in electronics or to strengthen materials without adding much weight, such as in tennis racket frames.

Greetings in the Caribbean — they're 'allo-tropical...

Before you go on, make sure you can explain the properties of all these allotropes of carbon.

Q1 Give three uses of fullerenes. [3 marks]

Metallic Bonding

Ever wondered what makes <u>metals</u> tick? Well, either way, this is the page for you.

Metallic Bonding Involves Delocalised Electrons

1) <u>Metals</u> also consist of a <u>giant structure</u>.
2) The electrons in the <u>outer shell</u> of the metal atoms are <u>delocalised</u> (free to move around). There are strong forces of <u>electrostatic attraction</u> between the <u>positive metal ions</u> and the shared <u>negative electrons</u>.
3) These forces of attraction <u>hold</u> the <u>atoms</u> together in a <u>regular</u> structure and are known as <u>metallic bonding</u>. Metallic bonding is very <u>strong</u>.

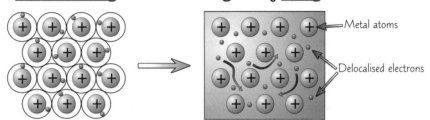

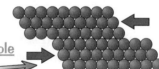

Metal atoms

Delocalised electrons

4) Substances that are held together by metallic bonding include metallic <u>elements</u> and <u>alloys</u> (see below).
5) It's the <u>delocalised electrons</u> in the metallic bonds which produce <u>all</u> the properties of metals.

Most Metals are Solid at Room Temperature

The electrostatic forces between the metal atoms and the delocalised sea of electrons are very <u>strong</u>, so need <u>lots of energy</u> to be broken.

This means that most compounds with metallic bonds have very <u>high</u> melting and boiling points, so they're generally <u>solid</u> at room temperature.

Metals are Good Conductors of Electricity and Heat

The <u>delocalised electrons</u> carry electrical current and thermal (heat) energy through the whole structure, so metals are good <u>conductors</u> of <u>electricity</u> and <u>heat</u>.

Most Metals are Malleable

The layers of atoms in a metal can <u>slide</u> over each other, making metals <u>malleable</u> — this means that they can be <u>bent</u> or <u>hammered</u> or <u>rolled</u> into <u>flat sheets</u>.

Alloys are Harder Than Pure Metals

1) <u>Pure metals</u> often aren't quite right for certain jobs — they're often <u>too soft</u> when they're pure so are <u>mixed</u> with other metals to make them <u>harder</u>. Most of the metals we use everyday are <u>alloys</u> — a <u>mixture</u> of <u>two or more metals</u> or a <u>metal and another element</u>. Alloys are <u>harder</u> and so more useful than pure metals.
2) Different elements have <u>different sized atoms</u>. So when another element is mixed with a pure metal, the new metal atoms will <u>distort</u> the layers of metal atoms, making it more difficult for them to slide over each other. This makes alloys <u>harder</u> than pure metals.

I saw a metal on the bus once — he was the conductor...

If your knowledge of metals is still feeling a bit delocalised, the questions below will help...

Q1   Copper is a metallic element. Describe and explain what property of copper makes it suitable for using in electrical circuits. [2 marks]

Q2   Suggest why an alloy of copper, rather than pure copper, is used to make hinges for doors [1 mark]

Topic 2 — Bonding, Structure and Properties of Matter

States of Matter

Better get your thinking hat on, as <u>states of matter</u> really... err.. matter. You'll need to imagine the <u>particles</u> in a substance as little snooker balls. Sounds strange, but it's useful for explaining lots of stuff in chemistry.

The Three States of Matter — Solid, Liquid and Gas

Materials come in <u>three</u> different forms — <u>solid</u>, <u>liquid</u> and <u>gas</u>. These are the <u>three states of matter</u>. Which <u>state</u> something is at a certain temperature (<u>solid</u>, <u>liquid</u> or <u>gas</u>) depends on how <u>strong</u> the forces of attraction are between the particles of the material. How strong the forces are depends on <u>THREE THINGS</u>:

     a) the <u>material</u> (the structure of the substance and the type of bonds holding the particles together),

     b) the <u>temperature</u>,

     c) the <u>pressure</u>.

The particles could be atoms, ions or molecules.

You can use a <u>model</u> called <u>particle theory</u> to explain how the particles in a material behave in each of the three states of matter by considering each particle as a <u>small, solid, inelastic sphere</u>.

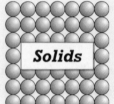

1) In solids, there are <u>strong forces</u> of attraction between particles, which holds them <u>close together</u> in <u>fixed positions</u> to form a very regular <u>lattice arrangement</u>.

2) The particles <u>don't move</u> from their positions, so all solids keep a <u>definite shape</u> and <u>volume</u>, and don't flow like liquids.

3) The particles <u>vibrate</u> about their positions — the <u>hotter</u> the solid becomes, the <u>more</u> they vibrate (causing solids to <u>expand</u> slightly when heated).

1) In liquids, there's a <u>weak force</u> of attraction between the particles. They're randomly arranged and <u>free</u> to <u>move</u> past each other, but they tend to <u>stick closely together</u>.

2) Liquids have a definite volume but <u>don't</u> keep a <u>definite shape</u>, and will flow to fill the bottom of a container.

3) The particles are <u>constantly</u> moving with <u>random motion</u>. The <u>hotter</u> the liquid gets, the <u>faster</u> they move. This causes liquids to <u>expand</u> slightly when heated.

1) In gases, the force of attraction between the particles is <u>very weak</u> — they're <u>free</u> to <u>move</u> and are <u>far apart</u>. The particles in gases travel in <u>straight lines</u>.

2) Gases <u>don't</u> keep a definite <u>shape</u> or <u>volume</u> and will always <u>fill</u> any container.

3) The particles move <u>constantly</u> with <u>random motion</u>. The <u>hotter</u> the gas gets, the <u>faster</u> they move. Gases either <u>expand</u> when heated, or their <u>pressure increases</u>.

Particle theory is a great <u>model</u> for explaining the three states of matter, but it <u>isn't perfect</u>. In reality, the particles aren't solid or inelastic and they aren't spheres — they're atoms, ions or molecules. Also, the model doesn't <u>show</u> the <u>forces</u> between the particles, so there's no way of knowing <u>how strong</u> they are.

State Symbols Tell You the State of a Substance in an Equation

You saw on page 15 how a chemical reaction can be shown using a <u>word equation</u> or <u>symbol equation</u>. Symbol equations can also include <u>state symbols</u> next to each substance — they tell you what <u>physical state</u> the reactants and products are in:

(s) — solid   (l) — liquid   (g) — gas   (aq) — aqueous

'Aqueous' means 'dissolved in water'.

For example, aqueous hydrochloric acid reacts with solid calcium carbonate to form aqueous calcium chloride, liquid water and carbon dioxide gas:

$$2HCl_{(aq)} + CaCO_{3(s)} \rightarrow CaCl_{2(aq)} + H_2O_{(l)} + CO_{2(g)}$$

Phew, what a page — particle-ularly gripping stuff...

I think it's pretty clever the way you can explain all the differences between solids, liquids and gases with just a page full of pink snooker balls. Anyway, that's the easy bit. The not-so-easy bit is learning it all.

Q1   Substance A does not have a definite shape or volume. What state is it in?   [1 mark]

Changing State

This page is like a game show. To start, everyone seems nice and solid, but turn up the <u>heat</u> and it all changes.

Substances Can Change from One State to Another

<u>Physical changes</u> don't change the particles — just their <u>arrangement</u> or their <u>energy</u>.

1) When a solid is <u>heated</u>, its particles gain more <u>energy</u>.

2) This makes the particles vibrate <u>more</u>, which <u>weakens</u> the <u>forces</u> that hold the solid together.

3) At a <u>certain temperature</u>, called the <u>melting point</u> the particles have enough energy to <u>break free</u> from their positions. This is called <u>MELTING</u> and the <u>solid</u> turns into a <u>liquid</u>.

4) When a liquid is <u>heated</u>, again the particles get even <u>more</u> energy.

5) This energy makes the particles move <u>faster</u>, which <u>weakens</u> and <u>breaks</u> the bonds holding the liquid together.

6) At a <u>certain temperature</u>, called the <u>boiling point</u>, the particles have <u>enough</u> energy to <u>break</u> their bonds. This is <u>BOILING</u> (or <u>evaporating</u>). The <u>liquid</u> becomes a <u>gas</u>.

Solid

melting | freezing

Liquid

boiling | condensing

Gas

12) At the <u>melting point</u>, so many bonds have formed between the particles that they're <u>held in place</u>. The <u>liquid</u> becomes a <u>solid</u>. This is <u>FREEZING</u>.

11) There's not enough energy to overcome the attraction between the particles, so more <u>bonds</u> form between them.

10) When a <u>liquid cools</u>, the particles have <u>less energy</u>, so move around less.

9) At the <u>boiling point</u>, so many bonds have formed between the gas particles that the <u>gas</u> becomes a <u>liquid</u>. This is called <u>CONDENSING</u>.

8) <u>Bonds form</u> between the particles.

7) As a gas <u>cools</u>, the particles no longer have <u>enough energy</u> to overcome the forces of attraction between them.

So, the amount of energy needed for a substance to change state depends on <u>how strong</u> the forces between particles are. The <u>stronger</u> the forces, the <u>more energy</u> is needed to break them, and so the <u>higher</u> the melting and boiling points of the substance.

You Have to be Able to Predict the State of a Substance

You might be asked to predict <u>what state</u> a substance is in at a <u>certain temperature</u>. If the temperature's <u>below</u> the <u>melting point</u> of substance, it'll be a <u>solid</u>. If it's <u>above</u> the <u>boiling point</u>, it'll be a <u>gas</u>. If it's <u>in between</u> the two points, then it's a <u>liquid</u>.

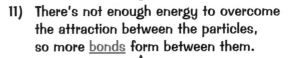
The bulk properties such as the melting point of a material depend on how lots of atoms interact together. An atom on its own doesn't have these properties.

EXAMPLE: Which of the molecular substances in the table is a liquid at room temperature (25 °C)?

	melting point	boiling point
oxygen	−219 °C	−183 °C
nitrogen	−210 °C	−196 °C
bromine	−7 °C	59 °C

Oxygen and nitrogen have boiling points below 25 °C, so will both be gases at room temperature.

So the answer's **bromine**. It melts at −7 °C and boils at 59 °C. So, it'll be a liquid at room temperature.

Some people are worth melting for...

Make sure you can describe what happens to particles, and the forces between them, as a substance is heated and cooled. Then learn all the technical terms, and you'll sound like a states of matter pro.

Q1 Ethanol melts at −114 °C and boils at 78 °C. Predict the state that ethanol is in at:
  a) −150 °C b) 0 °C c) 25 °C d) 100 °C [4 marks]

Topic 2 — Bonding, Structure and Properties of Matter

Nanoparticles

Just time to squeeze in something really small before the end of the topic...

Nanoparticles Are Really Really Really Really Tiny

...smaller than that.

Particles are put into categories depending on their diameter. For example:

Coarse particles (PM$_{10}$) have a diameter between 2500 nm (2.5×10^{-6} m) and 10 000 nm (1×10^{-5} m). They're also called dust.

Fine particles (PM$_{2.5}$) have a diameter between 100 nm (1×10^{-7} m) and 2500 nm (2.5×10^{-6} m).

Nanoparticles have a diameter between 1 nm (1×10^{-9} m) and 100 nm (1×10^{-7} m). These are particles that contain only a few hundred atoms.

1 nm = 0.000 000 001 m
(Like I said — really tiny.)

A typical atom has a diameter of about 0.1 nm (1×10^{-10} m).

There's a whole area of science that investigates the uses and properties of nanoparticles, called nanoscience.

Nanoparticles Have a Large Surface Area to Volume Ratio

1) The surface area to volume ratio is an important factor as it can affect the way that a particle behaves.

> surface area to volume ratio = surface area ÷ volume

2) As particles decrease in size, the size of their surface area increases in relation to their volume. This causes the surface area to volume ratio to increase.

Nannyparticles

3) You can see this happening by using two cubes as an example:

EXAMPLE:

Find the surface area to volume ratio for each of the cubes below.

This cube has sides of length 100 nm.

Each face has a surface area of 100 nm × 100 nm = 10 000 nm^2

The cube has six faces, so the total surface area is 6 × 10 000 nm^2 = 60 000 nm^2

The volume of the cube is 100 nm × 100 nm × 100 nm = 1 000 000 nm^3

The surface area to volume ratio = surface area ÷ volume = 60 000 ÷ 1 000 000 = 0.06 nm^{-1}

100 nm

The drawings of the cubes aren't to scale. Obviously.

10 nm

This cube has sides of length 10 nm.

Each face has a surface area of 10 nm × 10 nm = 100 nm^2

The cube has six faces, so the total surface area is 6 × 100 nm^2 = 600 nm^2

The volume of the cube is 10 nm × 10 nm × 10 nm = 1000 nm^3

The surface area to volume ratio = surface area ÷ volume = 600 ÷ 1000 = 0.6 nm^{-1}

As you decrease the side of any cube by a factor of ten, the surface area to volume ratio will always increase by a factor of ten.

4) Nanoparticles have a very high surface area to volume ratio — this means the surface area is very large compared to the volume.

5) This can cause the properties of a material to be different depending on whether it's a nanoparticle or whether it's in bulk. For example, you'll often need less of a material that's made up of nanoparticles to work as an effective catalyst compared to a material made up of 'normal' sized particles (containing billions of atoms rather than a few hundred).

Nano nano nano nano nano nano nano nano — particles...

Nanoparticles are between ten and one hundred times larger than atoms and molecules. That's teeny tiny.

Q1 Roughly what size are the particles studied in nanoscience? [1 mark]

Q2 a) The sides of a cube are 50 nm long. What's its surface to volume ratio? [3 marks]
b) Predict how the surface to volume area would change if the size of the cube was increased so its sides had a length of 500 nm. [2 marks]

Uses of Nanoparticles

'What's the use of something so small that not even a gnat can see it?' I hear you cry. Well, as you're about to find out, scientists have developed some pretty swanky uses for nanoparticles.

Nanoparticles Can Be Used in Lots of Things

Finding new ways to use nanoparticles is a really important area of scientific research. Here are some of the uses that have already been developed...

1) They have a huge surface area to volume ratio, so they could help make new catalysts.

2) Nanomedicine is a hot topic. The idea is that tiny particles (such as fullerenes from page 34) are absorbed more easily by the body than most particles. This means they could deliver drugs right into the cells where they're needed.

3) Some nanoparticles conduct electricity, so they can be used in tiny electric circuits for computer chips.

4) Silver nanoparticles have antibacterial properties. They can be added to polymer fibres that are then used to make surgical masks and wound dressings and they can also be added to deodorants.

5) Nanoparticles are also being used in cosmetics. For example, they're used to improve moisturisers without making them really oily.

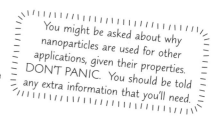
You might be asked about why nanoparticles are used for other applications, given their properties. DON'T PANIC. You should be told any extra information that you'll need.

The Effects of Nanoparticles on Health Aren't Fully Understood

1) Although nanoparticles are useful, the way they affect the body isn't fully understood, so it's important that any new products are tested thoroughly to minimise the risks.

2) Some people are worried that products containing nanoparticles have been made available before the effects on human health have been investigated properly, and that we don't know what the long-term impacts on health will be.

3) As the long-term impacts aren't known, many people believe that products containing nanoscale particles should be clearly labelled, so that consumers can choose whether or not to use them.

- Nanoparticles are being used in sun creams as they have been shown to be better than the materials in traditional sun creams at protecting skin from harmful UV rays.
- They also give better skin coverage than traditional sun creams.
- But it's not yet clear whether the nanoparticles can get into your body, and, if they do, whether they might damage cells.
- It's also possible that when they are washed away they might damage the environment.

Silver nanoparticles — to make jewellery for nanopeople...

If you thought you'd only ever meet nanoparticles in GCSE Chemistry, then think again. They've got loads of uses out there in the real world, so you'll be sure to hear more about them in the future. If you're still not sure what all the fuss is about, and why something so small might ever be any use, then have a go at the questions below

Q1   Give one potential application of nanoparticles that can conduct electricity.   [1 mark]

Q2   Nanoparticles may have applications in medicine.
      State one risk of using nanoparticles in this way.   [1 mark]

Q3   Both silver nanoparticles and titanium dioxide nanoparticles can be used to form a transparent layer.
      Silver nanoparticles conduct heat, whereas titanium dioxide nanoparticles are thermal insulators.
      State which of the nanoparticles could be used for making car windows that can quickly be
      defrosted in winter. Explain your answer.   [2 marks]

Revision Questions for Topic 2

And that's the end of Topic 2 — well, nearly the end. You still need to...
- ...try these questions and tick off each one when you get it right.
- When you've done all the questions under a heading and are completely happy with it, tick it off.

Ions and Ionic Compounds (p.28-30) ☐

1) What type of ion do elements from each of the following groups form?
   a) Group 1
   b) Group 7
2) Describe how an ionic bond forms.
3) Sketch dot and cross diagrams to show the formation of:
   a) sodium chloride   b) magnesium oxide   c) magnesium chloride   d) sodium oxide
4) Describe the structure of a crystal of sodium chloride.
5) List the main properties of ionic compounds.

Covalent Substances (p.31-34) ☐

6) Describe how covalent bonds form.
7) Sketch dot and cross diagrams showing the bonding in a molecule of:
   a) hydrogen   b) water   c) hydrogen chloride
8) Explain why simple molecular compounds typically have low melting and boiling points.
9) Describe the structure of a polymer.
10) Give three examples of giant covalent substances.
11) Explain why graphite can conduct electricity.
12) Explain how fullerenes could be used to deliver drugs into the body.

Metallic Bonding (p.35) ☐

13) What is metallic bonding?
14) List three properties of metals and explain how metallic structure causes each property.
15) Explain why alloys are harder than pure metals.

States of Matter (p.36-37) ☐

16) Name the three states of matter. *solid, liquid & gas*
17) What is the state symbol of an aqueous substance? *(aq)*
18) What is the name of the temperature at which a liquid becomes a gas? *boiling*
19) How does the strength of the forces between particles influence the temperature at which a substance changes state?

Nanoparticles and their Uses (p.38-39) ☐

20) What is nanoscience?
21) Give three uses of nanoparticles.
22) Explain why people may be wary of using products that contain nanoparticles.

Relative Formula Mass

Calculating <u>relative formula mass</u> is straight forward enough, but things can get a bit more confusing when you start working out the <u>percentage compositions</u> of compounds. Best get cracking, I suppose...

Compounds Have a Relative Formula Mass, M_r

If you have a compound like $MgCl_2$ then it has a <u>relative formula mass</u>, M_r, which is just the relative atomic masses of all the atoms in the molecular formula <u>added together</u>.

EXAMPLE: Find the relative formula mass of $MgCl_2$.

1) Look up the <u>relative atomic masses</u> of all the elements in the compound on the periodic table. (In the exams, you might be given the A_r you need in the question.) A_r of Mg = 24 and the A_r of Cl = 35.5.

2) <u>Add up</u> all the relative atomic masses of the atoms in the compound. $Mg + (2 \times Cl) = 24 + (2 \times 35.5) = 95$ So M_r of $MgCl_2$ = **95**

There are two chlorine atoms in $MgCl_2$, so the relative atomic mass of chlorine needs to be multiplied by 2.

You can find the relative atomic mass (A_r) of an element from the periodic table — it's the same as its mass number. See page 13 for more.

You Can Calculate the % Mass of an Element in a Compound

This is actually <u>dead easy</u> — so long as you've learnt this <u>formula</u>:

$$\text{Percentage mass of an element in a compound} = \frac{A_r \times \text{number of atoms of that element}}{M_r \text{ of the compound}} \times 100$$

EXAMPLE:

Find the percentage mass of sodium in sodium carbonate, Na_2CO_3.

A_r of sodium = 23, A_r of carbon = 12, A_r of oxygen = 16

M_r of $Na_2CO_3 = (2 \times 23) + 12 + (3 \times 16) = 106$

Percentage mass of sodium = $\dfrac{A_r \times \text{number of atoms of that element}}{M_r \text{ of the compound}} \times 100 = \dfrac{23 \times 2}{106} \times 100 = $ **43%**

You might also come across more complicated questions where you need to work out the percentage mass.

EXAMPLE:

A mixture contains 20% iron ions by mass. What mass of iron chloride ($FeCl_2$) would you need to provide the iron ions in 50 g of the mixture? A_r of Fe = 56, A_r of Cl = 35.5.

1) Find the <u>mass</u> of iron in the mixture.

The mixture contains 20% iron by mass, so in 50 g there will be $50 \times \dfrac{20}{100} = 10$ g of iron.

2) Calculate the <u>percentage mass</u> of iron in <u>iron chloride</u>.

$\text{Percentage mass of iron} = \dfrac{A_r \times \text{number of atoms of that element}}{M_r \text{ of the compound}} \times 100 = \dfrac{56}{56 + (2 \times 35.5)} \times 100 = 44.09...\%$

3) Calculate the <u>mass</u> of <u>iron chloride</u> that contains 10 g of iron.

Iron chloride contains 44.09% iron by mass, so there will be 10 g of iron in $10 \div \dfrac{44.09...}{100} = 23$ g

So you need **23 g** of iron chloride to provide the iron in 50 g of the mixture.

Relative mass — when you go to church with your parents...

The best way to get to grips with all this stuff is by practising. Start by having a go at these questions...

Q1   Calculate the relative formula mass (M_r) of: a) H_2O b) LiOH   c) H_2SO_4 [3 marks]

Q2   Calculate the percentage composition by mass of potassium in potassium hydroxide (KOH).   [2 marks]

The Mole

Moles can be pretty confusing. It's probably the word that puts people off. It's difficult to see the relevance of the word "mole" to anything but a small burrowing animal.

"The Mole" is Simply the Name Given to an Amount of a Substance

1) Just like "a million" is this many: 1 000 000; or "a billion" is this many: 1 000 000 000, so "the Avogadro constant" is this many: 602 000 000 000 000 000 000 000 or 6.02×10^{23}. And that's all it is. Just a number.

2) One mole of any substance is just an amount of that substance that contains an Avogadro number of particles — so 6.02×10^{23} particles. The particles could be atoms, molecules, ions or electrons.

3) The burning question, of course, is why is it such a silly long number like that, and with a 6 at the front?

4) The answer is that the mass of that number of atoms or molecules of any substance is exactly the same number of grams as the relative atomic mass (A_r) or relative formula mass (M_r) of the element or compound.

5) In other words, one mole of atoms or molecules of any substance will have a mass in grams equal to the relative formula mass (A_r or M_r) for that substance. Here are some examples:

> Carbon has an A_r of 12. So one mole of carbon weighs exactly 12 g.
> Nitrogen gas, N_2, has an M_r of 28 (2×14). So one mole of N_2 weighs exactly 28 g.
> Carbon dioxide, CO_2, has an M_r of 44 ($12 + [2 \times 16]$). So one mole of CO_2 weighs exactly 44 g.

6) This means that 12 g of carbon, or 28 g of N_2, or 44 g of CO_2, all contain the same number of particles, namely one mole or 6.023×10^{23} atoms or molecules.

Nice Formula to Find the Number of Moles in a Given Mass:

$$\text{Number of moles} = \frac{\text{mass in g (of an element or compound)}}{M_r \text{ (of the element or compound)}}$$

EXAMPLE: How many moles are there in 66 g of carbon dioxide (CO_2)?

1) Calculate the M_r of carbon dioxide. M_r of CO_2 = 12 + (16 × 2) = 44
2) Use the formula above to find out   No. of moles = Mass (g) ÷ M_r = 66 ÷ 44 = 1.5 mol
   how many moles there are.   Easy Peasy.

'mol' is the symbol for the unit 'moles'.

You can rearrange the equation above using this handy formula triangle. You could use it to find the mass of a known number of moles of a substance, or to find the M_r of a substance from a known mass and number of moles. Just cover up the thing you want to find with your finger and write down what's left showing.

$$\frac{\text{mass}}{\text{no. of moles} \times M_r}$$

EXAMPLE: What mass of carbon is there in 4 moles of carbon dioxide?

There are 4 moles of carbon in 4 moles of CO_2.
Cover up 'mass' in the formula triangle. That leaves you with 'no. of moles × M_r'.
So the mass of 4 moles of carbon = 4 × 12 = 48 g

What do moles have for pudding? Jam moly-poly...

Calculations involving moles can send some people into a spin. Don't be one of those people — there's really no need to freak out about moles. Go back over this page until you've got your head round it all.

Q1   Calculate the number of moles in 90 g of water (H_2O). A_r(O) = 16, A_r(H) = 1.   [2 marks]

Q2   Calculate the mass of 0.20 mol of potassium bromide (KBr). A_r(K) = 39, A_r(Br) = 80.   [2 marks]

Conservation of Mass

You've probably realised by now that you can't magic stuff out of thin air, and you can't make it magically disappear, either. This fact is pretty useful for working out the amounts of substances in chemical reactions.

In a Chemical Reaction, Mass is Always Conserved

1) During a chemical reaction no atoms are destroyed and no atoms are created.

2) This means there are the same number and types of atoms on each side of a reaction equation.

3) Because of this, no mass is lost or gained — we say that mass is conserved during a reaction.
   E.g.

$2Li + F_2 \rightarrow 2LiF$
In this reaction, there are 2 lithium atoms and 2 fluorine atoms on each side of the equation.

4) By adding up the relative formula masses of the substances on each side of a balanced symbol equation, you can see that mass is conserved. The total M_r of all the reactants equals the total M_r of the products.

   There's more about balanced symbol equations on p.15.

EXAMPLE:

Show that mass is conserved in this reaction: $2Li + F_2 \rightarrow 2LiF$.
1) Add up the relative formula masses on the left-hand side of the equation.
   $2 \times M_r(Li) + 2 \times M_r(F) = (2 \times 7) + (2 \times 19) = 14 + 38 = 52$
2) Add up the relative formula masses on the right-hand side of the equation.
   $2 \times M_r(LiF) = 2 \times (7 + 19) = 2 \times 26 = 52$

The total M_r on the left hand side of the equation is equal to the total M_r on the right hand side, so mass is conserved.

If the Mass Seems to Change, There's Usually a Gas Involved

In some experiments, you might observe a change of mass of an unsealed reaction vessel during a reaction. There are usually two explanations for this:

Explanation 1: If the mass increases, it's probably because one of the reactants is a gas that's found in air (e.g. oxygen) and all the products are solids, liquids or aqueous.

- Before the reaction, the gas is floating around in the air. It's there, but it's not contained in the reaction vessel, so you can't account for its mass.

- When the gas reacts to form part of the product, it becomes contained inside the reaction vessel — so the total mass of the stuff inside the reaction vessel increases.

For example, when a metal reacts with oxygen in an unsealed container, the mass of the container increases. The mass of the metal oxide produced equals the total mass of the metal and the oxygen that reacted from the air.

$$metal_{(s)} + oxygen_{(g)} \rightarrow metal\ oxide_{(s)}$$

Explanation 2: If the mass decreases, it's probably because one of the products is a gas and all the reactants are solids, liquids or aqueous.

- Before the reaction, all the reactants are contained in the reaction vessel.

- If the vessel isn't enclosed, then the gas can escape from the reaction vessel as it's formed. It's no longer contained in the reaction vessel, so you can't account for its mass — the total mass of the stuff inside the reaction vessel decreases.

For example, when a metal carbonate thermally decomposes to form a metal oxide and carbon dioxide gas, the mass of the reaction vessel will decrease if it isn't sealed. But in reality, the mass of the metal oxide and the carbon dioxide produced will equal the mass of the metal carbonate that decomposed.

$$metal\ carbonate_{(s)} \rightarrow metal\ oxide_{(s)} + carbon\ dioxide_{(g)}$$

Remember from the particle model on page 36 that a gas will expand to fill any container it's in. So if the reaction vessel isn't sealed, the gas expands out from the vessel, and escapes into the air around.

Leaving all the potatoes on your plate — that's mash conservation...

Never, ever forget that, in a reaction, the total mass of reactants is the same as the total mass of products.

Q1 Using the balanced equation, show that mass is conserved in the following reaction:

$H_2SO_{4(aq)} + 2NaOH_{(aq)} \rightarrow Na_2SO_{4(aq)} + 2H_2O_{(l)}$ $A_r(H) = 1, A_r(O) = 16, A_r(Na) = 23, A_r(S) = 32$ [5 marks]

The Mole and Equations

This is the moment where the 'number of moles = mass ÷ M_r' equation from page 42 comes into it's own.

You Can Use Moles to Calculate Masses in Reactions

Remember those balanced equations back on page 15? Well, the big numbers in front of the chemical formulas of the reactants and products tell you how many moles of each substance takes part or is formed during the reaction.

The little numbers tell you how many atoms of each element there are in each of the substances.

For example:

$$Mg_{(s)} + 2HCl_{(aq)} \rightarrow MgCl_{2(aq)} + H_{2(g)}$$

In this reaction, 1 mole of magnesium and 2 moles of hydrochloric acid react together to form 1 mole of magnesium chloride and 1 mole of hydrogen gas.

You Can Balance Equations Using Reacting Masses

If you know the masses of the reactants and products that took part in a reaction, you can work out the balanced symbol equation for the reaction. Here are the steps you should take:

1)   Divide the mass of each substance by its relative formula mass to find the number of moles.

2)   Divide the number of moles of each substance by the smallest number of moles in the reaction.

3)   If any of the numbers aren't whole numbers, multiply all the numbers by the same amount so that they all become whole numbers.

4)   Write the balanced symbol equation for the reaction by putting these numbers in front of the chemical formulas.

EXAMPLE: 8.1 g of zinc oxide (ZnO) reacts completely with 0.60 g of carbon to form 2.2 g of carbon dioxide and 6.5 g of zinc. Write a balanced symbol equation for this reaction. $A_r(C) = 12$, $A_r(O) = 16$, $A_r(Zn) = 65$.

1)   Work out M_r for each of the substances in the reaction:
   ZnO: 65 + 16 = 81   C: 12 CO_2: 12 + (2 × 16) = 44   Zn: 65

2)   Divide the mass of each substance by its M_r to calculate how many moles of each substance reacted or were produced:

$$ZnO: \frac{8.1}{81} = 0.10 \text{ mol} \qquad C: \frac{0.60}{12} = 0.050 \text{ mol}$$

$$CO_2: \frac{2.2}{44} = 0.050 \text{ mol} \qquad Zn: \frac{6.5}{65} = 0.10 \text{ mol}$$

3)   Divide by the smallest number of moles, which is 0.050:

$$ZnO: \frac{0.10}{0.050} = 2.0 \qquad C: \frac{0.050}{0.050} = 1.0$$

$$CO_2: \frac{0.050}{0.050} = 1.0 \qquad Zn: \frac{0.10}{0.050} = 2.0$$

These numbers give the ratio of the amounts of each substance in the reaction equation.

4)   The numbers are all whole numbers, so you can write out the balanced symbol equation straight away:

$$2ZnO + C \rightarrow CO_2 + 2Zn$$

Where do moles live? Edinburrow...

The calculations on this page have lots of steps, so the best way to learn how to do them is by practising. Luckily, there are some questions below to get you started. Don't say I don't spoil you. Better get cracking...

Q1   84 g of N_2 reacts completely with 18 g of H_2 to produce 102 g of NH_3.
   $M_r(N_2) = 28$, $M_r(H_2) = 2$, $M_r(NH_3) = 17$.
   a)   Calculate how many moles of each substance reacted or was produced.   [3 marks]
   b)   Use your answer to part a) to write a balanced symbol equation for this reaction.   [2 marks]

Limiting Reactants

Reactions don't go on forever — you need stuff in the reaction flask that can react. If one reactant gets completely used up in a reaction before the rest, then the reaction will stop. That reactant's called limiting.

Reactions Stop When One Reactant is Used Up

When some magnesium carbonate ($MgCO_3$) is placed into a beaker of hydrochloric acid, you can tell a reaction is taking place because you see lots of bubbles of gas being given off. After a while, the amount of fizzing slows down and the reaction eventually stops...

1) The reaction stops when all of one of the reactants is used up. Any other reactants are in excess. They're usually added in excess to make sure that the other reactant is used up.

2) The reactant that's used up in a reaction is called the limiting reactant (because it limits the amount of product that's formed).

3) The amount of product formed is directly proportional to the amount of limiting reactant. For example, if you halve the amount of limiting reactant the amount of product formed will also halve. If you double the amount of limiting reactant the amount of product will double (as long as it is still the limiting reactant).

4) This is because if you add more reactant there will be more reactant particles to take part in the reaction, which means more product particles.

The Amount of Product Depends on the Limiting Reactant

You can calculate the mass of a product formed in a reaction by using the mass of the limiting reactant and the balanced reaction equation.

You could also use this method to find the mass of a reactant needed to produce a known mass of a product.

1) Write out the balanced equation.
2) Work out relative formula masses (M_r) of the reactant and product you want.
3) Find out how many moles there are of the substance you know the mass of.
4) Use the balanced equation to work out how many moles there'll be of the other substance. In this case, that's how many moles of product will be made of this many moles of reactant.
5) Use the number of moles to calculate the mass.

EXAMPLE: Calculate the mass of aluminium oxide formed when 135 g of aluminium is burned in air.

1) Write out the balanced equation: $4Al + 3O_2 \rightarrow 2Al_2O_3$

2) Calculate the relative formula masses: Al: 27 Al_2O_3: $(2 \times 27) + (3 \times 16) = 102$

3) Calculate the number of moles of aluminium in 135 g: $\text{Moles} = \frac{\text{mass}}{M_r} = \frac{135}{27} = 5$ *You don't have to find M_r of oxygen because it's in excess.*

4) Look at the ratio of moles in the equation: 4 moles of Al react to produce 2 moles of Al_2O_3 — half the number of moles are produced.
   If the question asked for the number of moles of aluminium oxide formed, you'd stop here.   So 5 moles of Al will react to produce 2.5 moles of Al_2O_3

5) Calculate the mass of 2.5 moles of aluminium oxide: mass = moles × M_r = 2.5 × 102 = **255 g**

The mass of product (in this case aluminium oxide) is called the yield of a reaction. Masses you calculate in this way are called theoretical yields. In practice you never get 100% of the yield, so the amount of product you get will be less than you calculated.

'A Rush of Mud to the Head' — my favourite album by Moldplay...

I've said it before, I'll say it again — practice makes perfect. So before you get distracted by a cute picture of a kitten, or wander off to have a cup of tea, have a go at the question below.

Q1   The balanced equation for the reaction between chlorine and potassium bromide is:
$$Cl_2 + 2KBr \rightarrow Br_2 + 2KCl$$
Calculate the mass of potassium chloride produced when 23.8 g of potassium bromide reacts in an excess of chlorine. $A_r(K) = 39$, $A_r(Br) = 80$, $A_r(Cl) = 35.5$.   [4 marks]

Gases and Solutions

Time to find out how to calculate amounts of gases from <u>volumes</u> and amounts of solutes from <u>concentrations</u>.

One Mole of Any Gas Occupies 24 dm³ at 20 °C

At the same <u>temperature</u> and <u>pressure</u>, <u>equal numbers of moles</u> of <u>any gas</u> will occupy the same <u>volume</u>.

At <u>room temperature and pressure</u> (r.t.p. = 20 °C and 1 atm) one mole of <u>any</u> gas occupies <u>24 dm³</u>. You can use this formula to find the volume of a known mass of <u>any</u> gas at r.t.p.:

$$\text{Volume of gas} = \frac{\text{Mass of gas}}{M_r \text{ of gas}} \times 24$$

in dm³ — in g

 **EXAMPLE:**

What's the volume of 319.5 g of chlorine at r.t.p? $\text{Volume} = \frac{\text{Mass}}{M_r} \times 24 = \frac{319.5}{71} \times 24 = 108 \text{ dm}^3$

You Can Calculate Volumes of Gases in Reactions

For reactions between <u>gases</u>, you can use the <u>volume</u> of one gas to find the volume of another.

 **EXAMPLE:**

How much carbon dioxide is formed when 30 dm³ of oxygen reacts with carbon monoxide? $2CO_{(g)} + O_{2(g)} \rightarrow 2CO_{2(g)}$

1 mole of $O_2 \rightarrow$ 2 moles of CO_2 so 1 volume of $O_2 \rightarrow$ 2 volumes of CO_2

So 30 dm³ of $O_2 \rightarrow$ (2 × 30 dm³) = 60 dm³ of CO_2

Concentration is a Measure of How Crowded Things Are

1) Lots of reactions in chemistry take place between substances that are <u>dissolved</u> in a solution. The <u>amount</u> of a substance (e.g. the mass or the number of moles) in a certain <u>volume</u> of a solution is called its <u>concentration</u>.

2) The <u>more solute</u> (the substance that's dissolved) there is in a given volume, the <u>more concentrated</u> the solution.

3) One way to <u>measure</u> the concentration of a solution is by calculating the <u>mass</u> of a substance in a given <u>volume</u> of solution. The units will be <u>units of mass/units of volume</u>. Here's how to calculate the concentration of a solution in g/dm³:

$$\text{concentration} = \frac{\text{mass of solute}}{\text{volume of solvent}}$$

in g/dm³ — in g — in dm³

4) You can calculate the <u>mass</u> of a solute in solution by rearranging this formula to: <u>mass = conc. × volume</u>.

5) Concentration can also be given in <u>mol/dm³</u>:

in mol/dm³

$$\text{concentration} = \frac{\text{number of moles of solute}}{\text{volume of solvent}}$$

in mol — in dm³

 **EXAMPLES:**

1) What's the concentration in g/dm³ of a solution of sodium chloride where 30 g of sodium chloride is dissolved in 0.2 dm³ of water?

$\text{concentration} = \frac{30}{0.2} = 150 \text{ g/dm}^3$

1 dm³ = 1000 cm³

2) What's the concentration, in mol/dm³, of a solution with 2 moles of salt in 500 cm³?

- Convert the volume to <u>dm³</u> by dividing by 1000: 500 cm³ ÷ 1000 = 0.5 dm³
- Now you've got the number of moles and the volume in the right units, just stick them in the formula: $\text{Concentration} = \frac{2}{0.5} = 4 \text{ mol/dm}^3$

Gavin wasn't great at concentration.

CGP Revision Guides — not from concentrate...

It's pretty handy that any gas, yes I mean ANY gas, occupies the same volume under the same conditions.

Q1 Calculate the volume of 3.5 g of nitrogen (N_2) gas at room temperature and pressure. [2 marks]

Concentration Calculations

Ever found yourself wondering how to find the <u>concentration</u> of a solution from the concentration of a <u>different</u> solution and a couple of <u>volume</u> values? No? Oh well, here's how to do it anyway.

You Might Be Asked to Calculate the Concentration

<u>Titrations</u> are experiments that let you find the <u>volumes</u> needed for two solutions to <u>react together completely</u> (see p.52). If you know the <u>concentration</u> of one of the solutions, you can use the volumes from the titration experiment, along with the <u>reaction equation</u>, to <u>find</u> the concentration of the other solution.

Find the Concentration in mol/dm³

You might remember the formula for working out the <u>concentration</u> of a substance in mol/dm³ from page 46. Well, here it is in a handy <u>formula triangle</u>. It's dead useful in these calculations.

$$\frac{\text{no. of moles}}{\text{conc.} \times \text{volume}}$$

EXAMPLE: A student started with 30.0 cm³ of sulfuric acid (H_2SO_4) of unknown concentration in a flask. She found that it took an average of 25.0 cm³ of 0.100 mol/dm³ sodium hydroxide (NaOH) to neutralise the sulfuric acid. Find the concentration of the acid in mol/dm³. The balanced symbol equation for the reaction is: $2NaOH + H_2SO_4 \rightarrow Na_2SO_4 + 2H_2O$

1) Work out how many <u>moles</u> of the "<u>known</u>" substance you have using the formula: no. of moles = conc. × volume.
   0.100 mol/dm³ × (25.0 / 1000) dm³ = 0.00250 moles of NaOH

2) Use the reaction equation to work out how many moles of the "<u>unknown</u>" stuff you must have had.
   Using the equation, you can see that two moles of sodium hydroxide reacts with one mole of sulfuric acid.
   So 0.00250 moles of NaOH must have reacted with 0.00250 ÷ 2 = 0.00125 moles of H_2SO_4.

3) Work out the concentration of the "<u>unknown</u>" stuff.   *Make sure the volume is in dm³.*   *Don't round your answer until right at the end.*
   Concentration = number of moles ÷ volume
   = 0.00125 mol ÷ (30.0 ÷ 1000) dm³ = 0.041666... mol/dm³ = **0.0417 mol/dm³**

Remember — all measurements have some uncertainty to them. Titration experiments will often be repeated, and then the average (mean) of these repeated measurements will be calculated. The range of the results can also be found (see p.7), and can be used to give you an idea of how uncertain the mean value is (see p.11).

Converting mol/dm³ to g/dm³

1) To find the concentration in <u>g/dm³</u>, start by finding the concentration in mol/dm³ using the steps above.

You can also convert from g/dm³ to mol/dm³ by rearranging this equation to: moles = mass ÷ M_r

2) Then, <u>convert</u> the concentration in mol/dm³ to g/dm³ using the equation mass = moles × M_r.

EXAMPLE: What's the concentration, in g/dm³, of the sulfuric acid solution in the example above?

1) Work out the <u>relative formula mass</u> for the acid.
   $M_r(H_2SO_4) = (2 \times 1) + 32 + (4 \times 16) = 98$

2) Convert the concentration in <u>moles</u> (that you've already worked out) into concentration in <u>grams</u>. So, in 1 dm³:
   Mass in grams = moles × relative formula mass = 0.041666... × 98 = 4.08333... g
   So the concentration in g/dm³ = **4.08 g/dm³**

Time to convert my concentration from cat videos to chemistry...

These calculations look pretty scary. But if you get enough practice, then the fear will evaporate and you can tackle them with a smile on your face and a spring in your step. Better get cracking...

Q1   A student found that 22.5 cm³ of 0.150 mol/dm³ potassium hydroxide (KOH) was needed to neutralise 25.0 cm³ of nitric acid (HNO_3). The balanced equation for the reaction is: $HNO_3 + KOH \rightarrow KNO_3 + H_2O$
Calculate the concentration of nitric acid in mol/dm³.   [3 marks]

48

Atom Economy

It's important in industrial reactions that as much of the <u>reactants</u> as possible get turned into <u>useful products</u>. This depends on the <u>atom economy</u> and the <u>percentage yield</u> (see next page) of the reaction.

"Atom Economy" — % of Reactants Forming Useful Products

1) A lot of reactions make <u>more than one product</u>. Some of them will be <u>useful</u>, but others will be <u>waste</u>.

2) The <u>atom economy</u> (or atom utilisation) of a reaction tells you how much of the <u>mass</u> of the reactants is wasted when manufacturing a chemical and how much ends up as useful products. <u>Learn</u> the equation:

$$\text{atom economy} = \frac{\text{relative formula mass of desired products}}{\text{relative formula mass of all reactants}} \times 100$$

3) <u>100%</u> atom economy means that <u>all</u> the atoms in the reactants have been turned into <u>useful</u> (desired) <u>products</u>. The <u>higher</u> the atom economy the '<u>greener</u>' the process.

 **EXAMPLE:** Calculate the atom economy of the following reaction to produce hydrogen gas:

$$CH_4(g) + H_2O(g) \rightarrow CO(g) + 3H_2(g)$$

1) <u>Identify</u> the desired product — that's the <u>hydrogen gas</u>.
2) Work out the <u>M_r</u> of <u>all</u> the reactants:

$M_r(CH_4) = 12 + (4 \times 1) = 16$
$M_r(H_2O) = (2 \times 1) + 16 = 18$
$16 + 18 = 34$

3) Work out the <u>total M_r</u> of the <u>desired product</u>: $3 \times M_r(H_2) = 3 \times (2 \times 1) = 6$ So in this reaction, over
4) Use the <u>formula</u> to calculate the atom economy: $\frac{6}{34} \times 100 = \textbf{17.6\%}$ — 80% of the starting materials are wasted.

High Atom Economy is Better for Profits and the Environment

1) Pretty obviously, if you're making <u>lots of waste</u>, that's a <u>problem</u>.

2) Reactions with low atom economy <u>use up resources</u> very quickly. At the same time, they make lots of <u>waste</u> materials that have to be <u>disposed</u> of somehow. That tends to make these reactions <u>unsustainable</u> — the raw materials will run out and the waste has to go somewhere.

3) For the same reasons, low atom economy reactions aren't usually <u>profitable</u>. Raw materials are often <u>expensive to buy</u>, and waste products can be expensive to <u>remove</u> and dispose of <u>responsibly</u>.

4) The best way around the problem is to find a <u>use</u> for the waste products rather than just <u>throwing them away</u>. There's often <u>more than one way</u> to make the product you want, so the trick is to come up with a reaction that gives <u>useful "by-products"</u> rather than useless ones.

5) The reactions with the <u>highest</u> atom economy are the ones that only have <u>one product</u>. Those reactions have an atom economy of <u>100%</u>. The more products there are, the lower the atom economy is likely to be.

Atom economy isn't the only factor to be considered when choosing which reaction to use to make a certain product. Things such as the <u>yield</u> (see next page), the <u>rate</u> of the reaction (see page 67) and the <u>position of equilibrium</u> for reversible reactions (see page 72) also need to be thought about. A reaction with a low atom economy, that produces <u>useful by-products</u>, might also be used.

Atom economy class — even less legroom than economy class...

You might get asked about an unfamiliar industrial reaction in the exam. Don't panic — whatever example they give you, the same stuff applies. Have a go at the question below, and you'll see what I mean...

Q1 The following two reactions, A and B, both produce NH_3:
A. $2NH_4Cl + 2CaO \rightarrow CaCl_2 + Ca(OH)_2 + 2NH_3$ B. $N_2 + 3H_2 \rightarrow 2NH_3$
$A_r(N) = 14$, $A_r(H) = 1$, $A_r(Cl) = 35.5$, $A_r(Ca) = 40$, $A_r(O) = 16$
a) Which reaction, A or B, has the higher atom economy? Explain your answer. [1 mark]
b) Calculate the atom economy for the production of NH_3 by reaction A. [5 marks]

Percentage Yield

Percentage yield tells you about the <u>overall success</u> of an experiment. It <u>compares</u> what you think <u>you should get</u> (theoretical yield) with what <u>you get in practice</u> (actual yield).

Percentage Yield Compares Actual and Theoretical Yield

The <u>amount of product</u> you get is known as the <u>yield</u>. The more reactants you start with, the higher the <u>actual yield</u> will be — that's pretty obvious. But the <u>percentage yield doesn't</u> depend on the amount of reactants you started with — it's a <u>percentage</u>.

1) Percentage yield is given by the formula:

$$\text{percentage yield} = \frac{\text{mass of product actually made (in g)}}{\text{maximum theoretical mass of product (in g)}} \times 100$$

This is just the <u>maximum theoretical yield</u>. It can be calculated from the <u>balanced reaction equation</u> (see p.45).

2) Percentage yield is <u>always</u> somewhere between 0 and 100%. 100% yield means that you got <u>all</u> the product you expected to get. 0% yield means that <u>no</u> reactants were converted into product, i.e. no product at all was <u>made</u>.

If you know the percentage yield and the maximum theoretical yield of the reaction, you can rearrange this equation to work out what the mass of product actually made would be.

3) Industrial processes should have as <u>high</u> a percentage yield as possible to <u>reduce waste</u> and <u>reduce costs</u>.

Yields are Always Less Than 100%

In real life, you <u>never</u> get a 100% yield. Some product or reactant <u>always</u> gets lost along the way — and that goes for big <u>industrial processes</u> as well as school lab experiments. How this happens depends on <u>what sort of reaction</u> it is and what <u>apparatus</u> is being used. Lots of things can go wrong, but three <u>common problems</u> are:

1) Not All Reactants React to Make a Product

In <u>reversible reactions</u> (see page 72), the products can <u>turn back</u> into reactants, so the yield will <u>never</u> be <u>100%</u>.

For example, in the Haber process, at the same time as the reaction $N_2 + 3H_2 \rightarrow 2NH_3$ is taking place, the <u>reverse</u> reaction $2NH_3 \rightarrow N_2 + 3H_2$ is <u>also</u> happening.

This means the reaction $N_2 + 3H_2 \rightarrow 2NH_3$ <u>never</u> goes to <u>completion</u> (the reactants don't all get used up).

2) There Might be Side Reactions

The reactants sometimes react <u>differently</u> to how you expect. They might react with gases in the <u>air</u>, or <u>impurities</u> in the reaction mixture, so they end up forming <u>extra products</u> other than the ones you want.

3) You Lose Some Product When You Separate It From the Reaction Mixture

When you <u>filter a liquid</u> to remove <u>solid particles</u>, you nearly always lose a bit of liquid or a bit of solid.

- If you want to <u>keep the liquid</u>, you'll lose the bit that remains with the solid and filter paper (as they always stay a bit wet).
- If you want to <u>keep the solid</u>, some of it'll get left behind when you scrape it off the filter paper.

You'll also lose a bit of material when you <u>transfer</u> it from one container to another — even if you manage not to spill it. Some of it always gets left behind on the <u>inside surface</u> of the old container.

A yield of 100% in a reaction is pretty much impossible...

...but 100% in an exam is not. You just need luck on your side and to have learned your stuff really well.

Q1 A student carries out the following reaction: $Zn + 2HCl \rightarrow ZnCl_2 + H_2$. She calculates that her maximum theoretical yield of zinc chloride is 2.72 g. The actual yield after purification is 2.31 g.
Calculate the percentage yield of zinc chloride.
[1 mark]

Revision Questions for Topic 3

That's almost it for <u>Topic 3</u> — but before you go there are some questions to test <u>how much you really know</u>.

- Try these questions and <u>tick off each one</u> when you <u>get it right</u>.
- When you've done <u>all the questions</u> under a heading and are <u>completely happy</u> with it, tick it off.

<u>Moles and Equations (p.41-45)</u> ☑

1) How do you calculate the relative formula mass, M_r of a substance?
2) State the value of the Avogadro constant.
3) What is the formula that relates the number of moles of a substance to its mass and M_r?
4) What does conservation of mass mean?
5) Suggest why the mass of a reaction vessel might decrease during a reaction.
6) How can you determine the number of moles of each substance that would react together from the balanced reaction equation?
7) Explain what is meant by the term 'limiting reactant'.

<u>Volumes of Gases and Concentrations of Solutions (p.46-47)</u> ☑

8) What volume does one mole of any gas occupy at room temperature and pressure?
9) State the values of room temperature and pressure.
10) What is concentration?
11) Give the equation for working out the concentration of a solution in g/dm^3.
12) Give the equation for working out the concentration of a solution in mol/dm^3.
13) Describe how you would convert a concentration in mol/dm^3 to g/dm^3.

<u>Atom Economy and Percentage Yield (p.48-49)</u> ☑

14) Give the equation for calculating the atom economy of a reaction.
15) Give three reasons why it's better to use reactions that have a high atom economy.
16) What's the atom economy of a reaction that only produces one product?
17) What information do you need to find the theoretical yield of a reaction?
18) Give the equation for calculating the percentage yield of a reaction.
19) Give two reasons why it's better to use reactions with high percentage yields.
20) Give three reasons why percentage yield is always less than 100%.

Acids and Bases

Testing the pH of a solution means using an indicator — and that means pretty <u>co ours</u>...

The pH Scale Goes From 0 to 14

1) The <u>pH scale</u> is a measure of how <u>acidic</u> or <u>alkaline</u> a solution is.

2) The <u>lower</u> the pH of a solution, the <u>more acidic</u> it is.
    The <u>higher</u> the pH of a solution, the more <u>alkaline</u> it is.

3) A <u>neutral</u> substance (e.g. pure water) has <u>pH 7</u>.

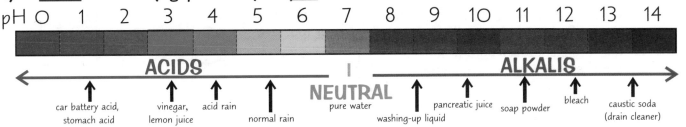

pH O 1 2 3 4 5 6 7 8 9 10 11 12 13 14

ACIDS | ALKALIS

NEUTRAL

car battery acid, stomach acid   vinegar, lemon juice   acid rain   normal rain   pure water   washing-up liquid   pancreatic juice   soap powder   bleach   caustic soda (drain cleaner)

You Can Measure the pH of a Solution

1) An <u>indicator</u> is a <u>dye</u> that <u>changes colour</u> depending on whether it's <u>above or below a certain pH</u>.
    Some indicators contain a <u>mixture of dyes</u> that means they <u>gradually change colour</u> over a
    broad range of pH. These are called <u>wide range indicators</u> and they're useful for <u>estimating</u> the
    pH of a solution. For example, <u>universal indicator</u> gives the colours shown above.

2) A <u>pH probe</u> attached to a <u>pH meter</u> can also be used to measure pH <u>electronically</u>.
    The probe is placed in the solution you are measuring and the pH is given on a
    digital display as a <u>numerical value</u>, meaning it's more accurate than an indicator.

Acids and Bases Neutralise Each Other

1) An <u>acid</u> is a substance that forms <u>aqueous solutions</u> with a pH of <u>less than 7</u>.
    Acids form H^+ ions in <u>water</u>.

2) A <u>base</u> is a substance with a pH <u>greater than 7</u>.

3) An <u>alkali</u> is a base that <u>dissolves in water</u> to form a solution
    with a pH <u>greater than 7</u>. Alkalis form <u>OH^- ions</u> in <u>water</u>.

The reaction between acids and bases is called <u>neutralisation</u>:

I have literally
no idea what
I'm doing.

$$ \text{acid} + \text{base} \rightarrow \text{salt} + \text{water} $$

Neutralisation between acids and alkalis can be seen in terms of <u>H^+</u> and <u>OH^- ions</u> like this:

$$ H^+_{(aq)} + OH^-_{(aq)} \rightarrow H_2O_{(l)} $$

Hydrogen (H^+) ions react with hydroxide
(OH^-) ions to produce water.

When an acid neutralises a base (or vice versa), the <u>products</u> are <u>neutral</u>, i.e. they have a <u>pH of 7</u>.
An indicator can be used to show that a neutralisation reaction is over.

<u>Neutralisation</u> reactions of <u>strong</u> acids and alkalis can be used to calculate the <u>concentration</u> of an acid or
alkali by <u>titration</u> — there is more about this technique on the next page.

This page should have all bases covered...

pHew, you finished the page... This stuff isn't too bad really, and pH is worth knowing about — it's important to
the chemistry in our bodies. For example, here's an interesting(ish) fact — your skin is slightly acidic (pH 5.5).

Q1   A student uses universal indicator to test the pH of some lemon juice.
      What colour would you expect the indicator to turn?   [1 mark]

Q2   The pH of an unknown solution is found to be 8. Is the solution acidic or alkaline?   [1 mark]

Titrations

PRACTICAL

Titrations are a method of analysing the <u>concentrations</u> of solutions. They're pretty important. Some people don't think they're the most exciting game in town. But I secretly enjoy them, now I've got the hang of them.

Titrations are Used to Find Out Concentrations

<u>Titrations</u> allow you to find out <u>exactly</u> how much acid is needed to <u>neutralise</u> a quantity of alkali — or vice versa. You can then use this data to work out the <u>concentration</u> of the acid or alkali (see page 47). For example:

You can also do titrations the other way round — adding alkali to acid.

1) Say you want to find out the concentration of some <u>alkali</u>. Using a <u>pipette</u> and <u>pipette filler</u>, add a set volume of the alkali to a <u>conical flask</u>. Add two or three drops of <u>indicator</u> too.

2) Use a <u>funnel</u> to fill a <u>burette</u> with some acid of <u>known concentration</u>. Make sure you do this **BELOW EYE LEVEL** — you don't want to be looking up if some acid spills over. (You should wear <u>safety glasses</u> too.) Record the <u>initial volume</u> of the acid in the burette.

3) Using the <u>burette</u>, add the <u>acid</u> to the alkali a bit at a time — giving the conical flask a regular <u>swirl</u>. Go especially <u>slowly</u> when you think the <u>end-point</u> (colour change) is about to be reached.

4) The indicator <u>changes colour</u> when <u>all</u> the alkali has been <u>neutralised</u>, e.g. phenolphthalein is <u>pink</u> in <u>alkaline</u> conditions, but <u>colourless</u> in <u>acidic</u> conditions.

5) <u>Record</u> the <u>final volume</u> of acid in the burette, and use it, along with the initial reading, to calculate the volume of acid used to <u>neutralise</u> the alkali.

Pipette
Pipettes measure only one volume of solution. Fill the pipette to about 3 cm above the line, then carefully drop the level down to the line.

① ②

Burette
Burettes measure different volumes and let you add the solution drop by drop.

acid

These marks down the side show the volume of acid used.

Conical flask containing alkali and indicator.

There's more about using burettes and pipettes on page 107.

- To increase the <u>accuracy</u> of your titration and to spot any <u>anomalous results</u>, you need <u>several consistent readings</u>.

- The <u>first</u> titration you do should be a <u>rough titration</u> to get an <u>approximate idea</u> of where the solution changes colour (the end-point).

- You then need to <u>repeat</u> the whole thing a few times, making sure you get (pretty much) the <u>same answer</u> each time (within 0.10 cm^3).

- Finally, calculate a <u>mean</u> of your results, ignoring any <u>anomalous results</u>.

Anomalous results are ones that don't fit in with the rest (see page 6).

Use Single Indicators for Titrations

1) <u>Universal indicator</u> is used to <u>estimate</u> the pH of a solution because it can turn a <u>variety of colours</u>. Each colour indicates a <u>narrow range</u> of pH values.

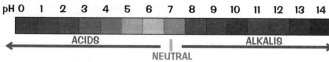

pH 0 1 2 3 4 5 6 7 8 9 10 11 12 13 14

ACIDS — NEUTRAL — ALKALIS

2) It's made from a <u>mixture</u> of different indicators. The colour <u>gradually</u> changes from red in acidic solutions to violet in alkaline solutions.

3) But during a titration between an alkali and an acid, you want to see a <u>sudden colour change</u>, at the end-point.

4) So you need to use a <u>single indicator</u>, such as <u>litmus</u> (blue in alkalis and red in acids), <u>phenolphthalein</u> (pink in alkalis and colourless in acids), or <u>methyl orange</u> (yellow in alkalis and red in acids).

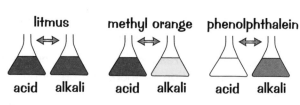

litmus   methyl orange   phenolphthalein

acid   alkali   acid   alkali   acid   alkali

How do you get lean molecules? Feed them tight rations...

Titrations aren't too tricky really — you just need to be as sure as you can be that your results are accurate, which means going slowly near the end-point and then repeating the whole process.

Q1   How do you determine when the end-point of a titration has been reached?   [1 mark]

Q2   Give two reasons why you should repeat a titration until you have consistent readings.   [2 marks]

Strong Acids and Weak Acids

I like <u>strong acids</u>, and I also like <u>weak acids</u>. But which is better? There's only one way to find out...

Acids Produce Protons in Water

The thing about acids is that they <u>ionise</u> in aqueous solution — they produce <u>hydrogen ions</u>, H^+.
For example:

$$HCl \rightarrow H^+ + Cl^-$$
$$HNO_3 \rightarrow H^+ + NO_3^-$$

An H^+ ion is just a proton.

These acids don't produce hydrogen ions until they meet water. So, for example, hydrogen chloride gas isn't acidic.

Acids Can be Strong or Weak

1) <u>Strong acids</u> (e.g. sulfuric, hydrochloric and nitric acids) <u>ionise completely</u> in water.
   All acid particles <u>dissociate</u> to release H^+ ions.

2) <u>Weak acids</u> (e.g. ethanoic, citric and carbonic acids) <u>do not fully ionise</u> in solution.
   Only a <u>small</u> proportion of acid particles dissociate to release H^+ ions.

3) The ionisation of a <u>weak</u> acid is a <u>reversible reaction</u>, which sets up an <u>equilibrium</u>
   between the <u>undissociated</u> and <u>dissociated acid</u>.
   Since only a few of the acid particles release H^+
   ions, the position of <u>equilibrium</u> lies well to the <u>left</u>.

   For more on equilibria turn to p.72.

   Strong acid: $HCl \longrightarrow H^+ + Cl^-$
   Weak acid: $CH_3COOH \rightleftharpoons H^+ + CH_3COO^-$

4) Reactions of acids involve the H^+ ions reacting with
   other substances. If the concentration of H^+ ions is <u>higher</u>, the <u>rate of reaction</u> will be
   faster, so <u>strong acids</u> will be <u>more reactive</u> than <u>weak acids</u> of the same concentration.

pH is a Measure of the Concentration of Hydrogen Ions

1) The <u>pH</u> of an acid or alkali is a measure of the <u>concentration</u> of H^+ ions in the solution.

2) For every <u>decrease</u> of 1 on the pH scale, the concentration of H^+ ions <u>increases</u> by a factor of <u>10</u>.
   So, an acid that has a pH of 4 has <u>10 times</u> the concentration of H^+ ions of an acid that has a pH of 5.
   For a decrease of 2 on the pH scale, the concentration of H^+ ions <u>increases</u> by a factor of <u>100</u>.
   The general rule for this is:

   $$\text{Factor } H^+ \text{ ion concentration changes by} = 10^{-x}$$

   X is the difference in pH.
   So if pH falls from 7 to 4 the
   difference is −3, and the factor
   the H^+ ion concentration has
   increased by is $10^{-(-3)} = 10^3$.

3) So the pH of a <u>strong</u> acid is always <u>less</u> than the pH
   of a <u>weaker</u> acid if they have the <u>same concentration</u>.

Don't Confuse Strong Acids with Concentrated Acids

1) Acid <u>strength</u> (i.e. strong or weak) tells you <u>what proportion</u> of the acid molecules <u>ionise</u> in water.

2) The <u>concentration</u> of an acid is different. Concentration measures
   <u>how much acid</u> there is in a certain volume of water.
   Concentration is basically how <u>watered down</u> your acid is.

   Concentration describes the total number of dissolved acid molecules — not the number of molecules that are ionised to produce hydrogen ions at any given moment.

3) The larger the amount of acid there is in a certain volume
   of liquid, the <u>more concentrated</u> the acid is.

4) So you can have a <u>dilute</u> (not very concentrated) but <u>strong</u> acid, or a <u>concentrated but weak</u> acid.

5) pH will <u>decrease</u> with <u>increasing</u> acid concentration <u>regardless</u> of whether it's a strong <u>or</u> weak acid.

Weak acid or strong acid? I know which goes better with chips...

Acids are acidic because of H^+ ions. And strong acids are strong because they let go of all their H^+ ions at the drop
of a hat... Well, at the drop of a drop of water.

Q1   Name a strong acid.   [1 mark]

Q2   A student added strong acid to a weakly acidic solution of pH 6. The pH of the new solution
      was found to be pH 3.   By how many times did the concentration of H^+ increase?   [1 mark]

Reactions of Acids

Remember neutralisation from page 51? Well, there's more stuff on <u>neutralisation reactions</u> coming up...

Metal Oxides and Metal Hydroxides are Bases

1) Some <u>metal oxides</u> and <u>metal hydroxides</u> dissolve in <u>water</u>. These soluble compounds are <u>alkalis</u>. As you saw on page 51, alkalis react with acids in <u>neutralisation reactions</u>.

2) Even <u>bases</u> that <u>won't dissolve</u> in water will still take part in neutralisation reactions with acids.

3) So, all <u>metal oxides</u> and <u>metal hydroxides</u> react with <u>acids</u> to form a <u>salt</u> and <u>water</u>.

Acid + Metal Oxide → Salt + Water   Acid + Metal Hydroxide → Salt + Water

The salt that's produced depends upon the <u>acid</u> and the <u>metal ion</u> in the <u>oxide</u> or <u>hydroxide</u>:

hydrochloric acid	+	copper oxide	→	copper chloride	+	water
$2HCl$	+	CuO	→	$CuCl_2$	+	H_2O
sulfuric acid	+	potassium hydroxide	→	potassium sulfate	+	water
H_2SO_4	+	$2KOH$	→	K_2SO_4	+	$2H_2O$
nitric acid	+	sodium hydroxide	→	sodium nitrate	+	water
HNO_3	+	$NaOH$	→	$NaNO_3$	+	H_2O

To work out the formula of an ionic compound, you need to balance the charges of the positive and negative ions so the overall charge of a compound is neutral. For more on ionic formulas, see p.30.

Acids and Metal Carbonates Produce Carbon Dioxide

Metal carbonates are also <u>bases</u>. They react with acids to produce a salt, water and <u>carbon dioxide</u>.

Acid + Metal Carbonate → Salt + Water + Carbon Dioxide

hydrochloric acid	+	sodium carbonate	→	sodium chloride	+	water	+	carbon dioxide
$2HCl$	+	Na_2CO_3	→	$2NaCl$	+	H_2O	+	CO_2
sulfuric acid	+	calcium carbonate	→	calcium sulfate	+	water	+	carbon dioxide
H_2SO_4	+	$CaCO_3$	→	$CaSO_4$	+	H_2O	+	CO_2

You can Make Soluble Salts Using an Insoluble Base

PRACTICAL

1) You need to pick the right <u>acid</u> and <u>insoluble base</u>, such as an <u>insoluble metal oxide</u>, <u>hydroxide</u> or <u>carbonate</u>. E.g. if you want to make <u>copper chloride</u>, you could mix <u>hydrochloric acid</u> and <u>copper oxide</u>. $CuO_{(s)} + 2HCl_{(aq)} \rightarrow CuCl_{2(aq)} + H_2O_{(l)}$

You could also react the acid with a metal.

2) Gently <u>warm</u> the dilute acid using a <u>Bunsen burner</u>, then turn off the Bunsen burner.

3) Add the <u>insoluble base</u> to the <u>acid</u> a bit at a time, until no more reacts (i.e. the base is in <u>excess</u>). You'll know when all the acid has been neutralised because, even after stirring, the excess solid will just <u>sink</u> to the bottom of the flask.

4) Then <u>filter</u> out the <u>excess</u> solid to get the salt solution (see p.17).

filter paper

filter funnel

5) To get <u>pure</u>, <u>solid</u> crystals of the <u>salt</u>, gently heat the solution using a <u>water bath</u> or an <u>electric heater</u> to evaporate some of the water (to make it more concentrated) and then stop heating it and leave the solution to cool. <u>Crystals</u> of the salt should form, which can be <u>filtered</u> out of the solution and then <u>dried</u>. This is called <u>crystallisation</u> (p.17).

AHHHHH so many reactions...

In the exam you could get asked to describe how you would go about making a pure, dry sample of a given soluble salt. Make sure you understand the method and what reactants to use.

Q1   Calcium carbonate is added to hydrochloric acid.
       Write a word equation for the reaction that occurs.

[2 marks]

The Reactivity Series

You can place <u>metals</u> in order of reactivity. This can be a lot more useful than it sounds, promise.

The Reactivity Series — How Well a Metal Reacts

1) The <u>reactivity series</u> lists metals in <u>order</u> of their <u>reactivity</u> towards other substances.

2) For metals, their reactivity is determined by how <u>easily</u> they lose electrons — forming positive ions. The <u>higher</u> up the reactivity series a metal is, the more easily they form <u>positive ions</u>. Make sure you learn this list: ➡

3) When metals <u>react</u> with <u>water</u> or <u>acid</u>, they <u>lose</u> electrons and form positive ions. So, the <u>higher</u> a metal is in the reactivity series, the more <u>easily</u> it <u>reacts</u> with water or acid.

4) If you <u>compare</u> the relative reactivity of different metals with either an <u>acid</u> or <u>water</u> and put them in order from <u>most</u> reactive to the <u>least</u> reactive, the order you get is the reactivity series.

The Reactivity Series

Potassium	K
Sodium	Na
Lithium	Li
Calcium	Ca
Magnesium	Mg
Carbon	C
Zinc	Zn
Iron	Fe
Hydrogen	H
Copper	Cu

Carbon and hydrogen are non-metals but are often included in the reactivity series.

Very Reactive

Fairly Reactive

Not very Reactive

How Metals React With Acids Tells You About Their Reactivity

Some metals react with acids to produce a <u>salt</u> and <u>hydrogen gas</u>.

Acid + Metal → Salt + Hydrogen

1) The <u>speed</u> of reaction is indicated by the <u>rate</u> at which the <u>bubbles</u> of hydrogen are given off.

2) The more <u>reactive</u> the metal, the <u>faster</u> the reaction will go. <u>Very</u> reactive metals like potassium, sodium, lithium and calcium react explosively, but less reactive metals such as magnesium, zinc and iron react less violently. In general, copper <u>won't</u> react with cold, dilute acids.

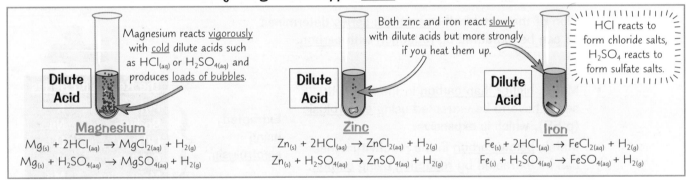

Magnesium reacts <u>vigorously</u> with <u>cold</u> dilute acids such as $HCl_{(aq)}$ or $H_2SO_{4(aq)}$ and produces <u>loads of bubbles</u>.

Both zinc and iron react <u>slowly</u> with dilute acids but more strongly if you heat them up.

HCl reacts to form chloride salts, H_2SO_4 reacts to form sulfate salts.

Dilute Acid — **Magnesium**
$$Mg_{(s)} + 2HCl_{(aq)} \rightarrow MgCl_{2(aq)} + H_{2(g)}$$
$$Mg_{(s)} + H_2SO_{4(aq)} \rightarrow MgSO_{4(aq)} + H_{2(g)}$$

Dilute Acid — **Zinc**
$$Zn_{(s)} + 2HCl_{(aq)} \rightarrow ZnCl_{2(aq)} + H_{2(g)}$$
$$Zn_{(s)} + H_2SO_{4(aq)} \rightarrow ZnSO_{4(aq)} + H_{2(g)}$$

Dilute Acid — **Iron**
$$Fe_{(s)} + 2HCl_{(aq)} \rightarrow FeCl_{2(aq)} + H_{2(g)}$$
$$Fe_{(s)} + H_2SO_{4(aq)} \rightarrow FeSO_{4(aq)} + H_{2(g)}$$

3) You can also investigate the reactivity of metals by measuring the <u>temperature change</u> of the reaction with an acid or water over a set time period. If you use the same <u>mass</u> and <u>surface area</u> of metal each time, then the <u>more reactive</u> the metal, the greater the temperature change should be.

Metals Also React with Water

The <u>reactions</u> of metals with <u>water</u> also show the reactivity of metals.

You can see more on the reactions of Group 1 metals with water on page 24.

Metal + Water → Metal Hydroxide + Hydrogen

For example, calcium: $Ca_{(s)} + 2H_2O_{(l)} \rightarrow Ca(OH)_{2(aq)} + H_{2(g)}$

1) The metals <u>potassium</u>, <u>sodium</u>, <u>lithium</u> and <u>calcium</u> will all react with water.

2) Less reactive metals like <u>zinc</u>, <u>iron</u> and <u>copper</u> won't react with water.

I AM NOT HIGHLY REACTIVE — OK...

See, experiments aren't just for fun — they can give you a thrilling insight into the relative reactivities of elements.

Q1   Give the balanced equation, including state symbols, for the reaction of sodium and water.   **[3 marks]**

Separating Metals From Metal Oxides

Most metals are not found in the earth as pure lumps. Instead, you have to <u>extract</u> them from a compound meaning more work is required. Thanks for nothing nature...

Metals Often Have to be Separated from their Oxides

1) Lots of common metals, like iron and aluminium, react with <u>oxygen</u> to form <u>oxides</u>. This process is an example of <u>oxidation</u>. These oxides are often the <u>ores</u> that the metals need to be extracted from.

2) A reaction that separates a metal from its oxide is called a <u>reduction reaction</u>.

> *An ore is a type of rock that contains metal compounds.*

FORMATION OF METAL ORE:

<u>Oxidation = Gain of Oxygen</u>

E.g. magnesium is <u>oxidised</u> to make magnesium oxide.

$$2Mg + O_2 \rightarrow 2MgO$$

EXTRACTION OF METAL:

<u>Reduction = Loss of Oxygen</u>

E.g. copper oxide is <u>reduced</u> to copper.

$$2CuO + C \rightarrow 2Cu + CO_2$$

Some Metals can be Extracted by Reduction with Carbon

1) Some metals can be <u>extracted</u> from their ores chemically by <u>reduction</u> using <u>carbon</u>.

2) In this reaction, the ore is <u>reduced</u> as oxygen is <u>removed</u> from it, and carbon <u>gains</u> oxygen so is <u>oxidised</u>. For example...

$2Fe_2O_3$	+	$3C$	$\rightarrow$	$4Fe$	+	$3CO_2$
iron(III) oxide	+	carbon	$\rightarrow$	iron	+	carbon dioxide

3) The position of the metal in the <u>reactivity series</u> determines whether it can be extracted by <u>reduction</u> with <u>carbon</u>.

I think I'm a bit lost.

- Metals <u>higher than carbon</u> in the reactivity series have to be extracted using <u>electrolysis</u> (p.58), which is expensive.
- Metals <u>below carbon</u> in the reactivity series can be extracted by <u>reduction</u> using <u>carbon</u>. For example, <u>iron oxide</u> is reduced in a <u>blast furnace</u> to make <u>iron</u>.
- This is because carbon <u>can only take the oxygen</u> away from metals which are <u>less reactive</u> than carbon <u>itself</u> is.

Extracted using <u>electrolysis</u>.

Extracted by <u>reduction</u> using <u>carbon</u>.

The Reactivity Series

Potassium	K	More Reactive
Sodium	Na	
Lithium	Li	
Calcium	Ca	
Magnesium	Mg	
<u>Carbon</u>	<u>C</u>	
Zinc	Zn	
Iron	Fe	
Copper	Cu	Less Reactive

Some metals are <u>so unreactive</u> they are in the earth as the metal <u>itself</u>. For example, <u>gold</u> is mined as its elemental form.

> *Make sure you can explain how and why different metals are extracted in different ways.*

Are you going to revise this page, ore what?

Metals are great aren't they? Loads of uses. Shame extracting them's not always cheap. Make sure you know the difference between reduction and oxidation and why carbon can be used to extract some metals but not others.

Q1   Write a balanced equation for the reduction of zinc oxide, ZnO, by carbon, C.   [2 marks]

Q2   A mining company tried to extract calcium from its ore by reduction with carbon. The process did not work. Explain why.   [1 mark]

Redox Reactions

In chemistry, oxidation <u>doesn't</u> just mean gain of oxygen. No, that would be far too easy.

If Electrons are Transferred, It's a Redox Reaction

1) Oxidation can mean the <u>addition of oxygen</u> (or a reaction with it), and reduction can be the <u>removal of oxygen</u>, but on this page we're looking at oxidation and reduction in terms of <u>electrons</u>.

2) A <u>loss of electrons</u> is called <u>oxidation</u>. A <u>gain of electrons</u> is called <u>reduction</u>. A handy way to remember this is by the mnemonic OIL RIG — <u>O</u>xidation <u>I</u>s <u>L</u>oss, <u>R</u>eduction <u>I</u>s <u>G</u>ain.

3) RED<u>uction</u> and OX<u>idation</u> happen <u>at the same time</u> — hence the term "REDOX".

- <u>Iron atoms</u> are <u>oxidised</u> to Fe^{2+} ions when they react with <u>dilute acid</u>: $Fe + 2H^+ \rightarrow Fe^{2+} + H_2$
- The <u>iron atoms lose electrons</u>. They're <u>oxidised</u> by the hydrogen ions: $Fe - 2e^- \rightarrow Fe^{2+}$
- The <u>hydrogen ions gain electrons</u>. They're <u>reduced</u> by the iron atoms: $2H^+ + 2e^- \rightarrow H_2$

All reactions of metals and acids on p.55 are redox reactions.

Displacement Reactions are Redox Reactions

1) <u>Displacement</u> reactions involve one metal <u>kicking another one out</u> of a compound. Here's the rule: ⟹ **A MORE REACTIVE metal will displace a LESS REACTIVE metal from its compound.**

2) If you put a <u>reactive metal</u> into the solution of a <u>dissolved metal compound</u>, the reactive metal will <u>replace</u> the <u>less reactive metal</u> in the compound (see the reactivity series on p.55).

If you put <u>iron</u> in a solution of <u>copper sulfate</u> ($CuSO_4$) the more reactive iron will '<u>kick out</u>' the less reactive copper from the solution. You end up with <u>iron sulfate solution</u> ($FeSO_4$) and <u>copper metal</u>.

$$\text{iron + copper sulfate} \rightarrow \text{iron sulfate + copper}$$
$$Fe_{(s)} + CuSO_{4(aq)} \rightarrow FeSO_{4(aq)} + Cu_{(s)}$$

In this reaction the iron <u>loses</u> 2 electrons to become a 2+ ion — it's <u>oxidised</u>. The copper ion <u>gains</u> these 2 electrons to become a copper atom — it's <u>reduced</u>.

$$Fe \rightarrow Fe^{2+} + 2e^- \qquad Cu^{2+} + 2e^- \rightarrow Cu$$

3) In displacement reactions, it's always the <u>metal ion</u> that gains electrons and is <u>reduced</u>. The <u>metal atom</u> always loses electrons and is <u>oxidised</u>.

4) In the exam you could be asked to write <u>word or symbol equations</u> to show displacement reactions.

Koalas are more reactive than rucksacks.

Ionic Equations Show Just the Useful Bits of Reactions

1) In an <u>ionic equation</u> only the particles that react and the products they form are shown. For example:

$$Mg_{(s)} + Zn^{2+}_{(aq)} \rightarrow Mg^{2+}_{(aq)} + Zn_{(s)}$$

2) This <u>just</u> shows the <u>displacement</u> of <u>zinc ions</u> by magnesium metal. Here's what the full equation of the above reaction would be if you'd started off with zinc chloride:

$$Mg_{(s)} + ZnCl_{2(aq)} \rightarrow MgCl_{2(aq)} + Zn_{(s)}$$

3) If you write out the equations so you can see all the ions, you'll see that the chloride ions <u>don't change</u> in the reaction — they're <u>spectator ions</u>. They're of no interest here so can be crossed out.

$$Mg_{(s)} + Zn^{2+}_{(aq)} + 2Cl^-_{(aq)} \rightarrow Mg^{2+}_{(aq)} + 2Cl^-_{(aq)} + Zn_{(s)}$$

4) Instead, the ionic equation for this displacement reaction just <u>concentrates</u> on the substances which are <u>oxidised</u> or <u>reduced</u>.

REDOX — great for bubble baths. Oh no, wait...

Ionic equations are hugely important in chemistry. Better practice until you can do them in your sleep.

Q1   The equation for the reaction of zinc and iron sulfate is: $Zn_{(s)} + FeSO_{4(aq)} \rightarrow ZnSO_{4(aq)} + Fe_{(s)}$
     a) Write an ionic equation for the reaction.   [1 mark]
     b) State which species is being reduced and which is being oxidised.   [2 marks]

Electrolysis

Electrolysis uses an <u>electrical current</u> to cause a reaction. It's actually pretty cool. No, really...

Electrolysis Means 'Splitting Up with Electricity'

1) During electrolysis, an electric current is passed through an electrolyte (a <u>molten</u> or <u>dissolved</u> ionic compound). The ions move towards the electrodes, where they react, and the compound <u>decomposes</u>.

2) The <u>positive ions</u> in the electrolyte will move towards the <u>cathode</u> (-ve electrode) and <u>gain</u> electrons (they are <u>reduced</u>).

An electrolyte is just a liquid or solution that can conduct electricity. An electrode is a solid that conducts electricity and is submerged in the electrolyte

3) The <u>negative ions</u> in the electrolyte will move towards the <u>anode</u> (+ve electrode) and <u>lose</u> electrons (they are <u>oxidised</u>).

4) This creates a <u>flow of charge</u> through the <u>electrolyte</u> as ions travel to the electrodes.

5) As ions gain or lose electrons, they form the uncharged element and are <u>discharged</u> from the electrolyte.

Electrolysis of Molten Ionic Solids Forms Elements

The electrodes should be inert so they don't react with the electrolyte.

1) An <u>ionic solid can't</u> be electrolysed because the ions are in fixed positions and <u>can't move</u>.

2) <u>Molten ionic compounds can</u> be electrolysed because the ions can <u>move freely</u> and conduct electricity.

3) Molten ionic liquids, e.g. lead bromide, are always broken up into their <u>elements</u>.

4) Positive <u>metal</u> ions are <u>reduced</u> to the element at the <u>cathode</u>: ⟶ $Pb^{2+} + 2e^- \rightarrow Pb$

5) Negative <u>non-metal</u> ions are <u>oxidised</u> to the element at the <u>anode</u>: ⟶ $2Br^- \rightarrow Br_2 + 2e^-$

Metals can be Extracted From Their Ores Using Electrolysis

If a metal is <u>too reactive</u> to be <u>reduced</u> with <u>carbon</u> (page 56) or reacts with carbon, then electrolysis can be used to extract it. Extracting metals via this method is very expensive as lots of energy is required to melt the ore and produce the required current.

1) Aluminium is extracted from the ore <u>bauxite</u> by <u>electrolysis</u>. Bauxite contains <u>aluminium oxide</u>, Al_2O_3.

2) Aluminium oxide has a <u>very high</u> melting temperature so it's mixed with <u>cryolite</u> to lower the melting point.

Cryolite is an aluminium based compound with a lower melting point than aluminium oxide.

3) The <u>molten mixture</u> contains <u>free ions</u> — so it'll <u>conduct electricity</u>.

4) The <u>positive Al^{3+} ions</u> are attracted to the <u>negative electrode</u> where they <u>each pick up three electrons</u> and turn into neutral <u>aluminium atoms</u>. These then <u>sink</u> to the bottom of the electrolysis tank.

5) The <u>negative O^{2-} ions</u> are attracted to the <u>positive electrode</u> where they <u>each lose two electrons</u>. The neutral oxygen atoms will then <u>combine</u> to form <u>O_2</u> molecules.

At the negative electrode:

Reduction — a gain of electrons:

$$Al^{3+} + 3e^- \rightarrow Al$$

<u>Metals</u> form <u>positive ions</u>, so they're attracted to the <u>negative</u> electrode.

<u>Aluminium</u> is produced at the <u>negative electrode</u>.

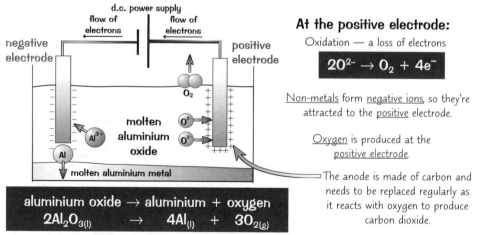

At the positive electrode:

Oxidation — a loss of electrons

$$2O^{2-} \rightarrow O_2 + 4e^-$$

<u>Non-metals</u> form <u>negative ions</u>, so they're attracted to the <u>positive</u> electrode.

<u>Oxygen</u> is produced at the <u>positive electrode</u>.

The anode is made of carbon and needs to be replaced regularly as it reacts with oxygen to produce carbon dioxide.

Overall Equation:

aluminium oxide → aluminium + oxygen

$$2Al_2O_{3(l)} \rightarrow 4Al_{(l)} + 3O_{2(g)}$$

Faster shopping at the supermarket — use Electrolleys...

It might be jolly useful for your exams to learn the products of electrolysis of molten lead bromide...

Q1   A student carries out electrolysis on molten sodium chloride. What is produced at:
a) the anode?   b) the cathode?

[2 marks]

Electrolysis of Aqueous Solutions

When you electrolyse an aqueous solution, you also have to factor in the ions in the <u>water</u>.

It May be Easier to Discharge Ions from Water than the Solute

1) In <u>aqueous solutions</u>, as well as the <u>ions</u> from the ionic compound, there will be <u>hydrogen ions</u> (H^+) and <u>hydroxide ions</u> (OH^-) from the <u>water</u>: $\quad H_2O_{(l)} \rightleftharpoons H^+_{(aq)} + OH^-_{(aq)}$

2) At the <u>cathode</u>, if <u>H^+ ions and metal ions</u> are present, <u>hydrogen gas</u> will be produced if the metal ions form an elemental metal that is <u>more reactive</u> than hydrogen (e.g. sodium ions). If the metal ions form an elemental metal that is <u>less reactive</u> than hydrogen (e.g. copper ions), a solid layer of the <u>pure metal</u> will be produced instead.

3) At the <u>anode</u>, if <u>OH^- and halide ions</u> (Cl^-, Br^-, I^-) are present, molecules of chlorine, bromine or iodine will be formed. If <u>no halide ions</u> are present, then the OH^- ions are discharged and <u>oxygen</u> will be formed.

A solution of <u>copper(II) sulfate</u> ($CuSO_4$) contains <u>four different ions</u>: Cu^{2+}, SO_4^{2-}, H^+ and OH^-.

- <u>Copper</u> metal is less reactive than hydrogen. So at the cathode, <u>copper metal</u> is produced and coats the electrode.

$$Cu^{2+} + 2e^- \rightarrow Cu$$

- There aren't any <u>halide ions</u> present. So at the anode <u>oxygen</u> and <u>water</u> are produced. The oxygen can be seen as <u>bubbles</u>.

$$4OH^- \rightarrow O_2 + 2H_2O + 4e^-$$

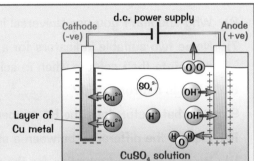

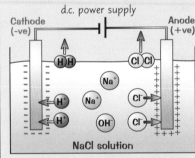

A solution of <u>sodium chloride</u> (NaCl) contains <u>four different ions</u>: Na^+, Cl^-, OH^- and H^+.

- <u>Sodium</u> metal is more reactive than hydrogen. So at the cathode, <u>hydrogen gas</u> is produced.

$$2H^+ + 2e^- \rightarrow H_2$$

- <u>Chloride ions</u> are present in the solution. So at the anode <u>chlorine gas</u> is produced.

$$2Cl^- \rightarrow Cl_2 + 2e^-$$

If you're drawing the apparatus for an electrolysis experiment, remember to include a d.c. power supply, wires and labels for the anode and the cathode. The anode is the electrode on the same side as the longer line of the d.c. power supply symbol.

PRACTICAL

You can set up an electrolysis <u>experiment</u> in the <u>lab</u> like the set-up on page 109. Once the experiment is finished you can <u>test</u> any <u>gaseous products</u> to work out what was produced.

- Chlorine <u>bleaches</u> damp <u>litmus paper</u>, turning it white.
- Hydrogen makes a "<u>squeaky pop</u>" with a <u>lighted splint</u>.
- Oxygen will <u>relight</u> a <u>glowing splint</u>.

For more on tests for gases, turn to page 88.

The Half Equations — Make Sure the Electrons Balance

<u>Half equations</u> show the reactions at the <u>electrodes</u>. The important thing to remember when you're <u>combining half equations</u> is that the <u>number of electrons</u> needs to be the <u>same</u> for each half equation. For the electrolysis of aqueous sodium chloride the half equations are:

<u>Negative Electrode:</u> $\quad 2H^+ + 2e^- \rightarrow H_2$

<u>Positive Electrode:</u> $\quad 2Cl^- \rightarrow Cl_2 + 2e^- \quad$ or $\quad 2Cl^- - 2e^- \rightarrow Cl_2$

These combine to form the ionic equation: $2H^+ + 2Cl^- \rightarrow H_2 + Cl_2$

The electrons on each side of the half equations balance, so they can be cancelled out in the full ionic equation.

When a halide <u>isn't</u> present in the aqueous solution, the half equation for the <u>anode</u> is:

$$4OH^- \rightarrow O_2 + 2H_2O + 4e^- \quad \text{or} \quad 4OH^- - 4e^- \rightarrow O_2 + 2H_2O$$

I wrote a poem about my tabby — it was a cat ode...

So it's kinda confusing this electrolysis malarkey — you need to take it slow and make sure you get it.

Q1   An aqueous solution of copper chloride, $CuCl_2$, is electrolysed using inert electrodes. Give the half equations for the anode and the cathode.

[2 marks]

Revision Questions for Topic 4

Another topic finished. Time to test your knowledge of chemical changes...
* Try these questions and <u>tick off each one</u> when you <u>get it right</u>.
* When you've done <u>all the questions</u> under a heading and are <u>completely happy</u> with it, tick it off.

<u>Acids and their Reactions (p.51-54)</u> ☑

1) State whether the following pH values are acidic, alkaline or neutral.
   a) 9   b) 2   c) 7   d) 6

2) Give the general word equation for the reaction between an acid and a base.

3) What type of reagent could be used to show that an acid or base has been completely neutralised?

4) Describe the steps involved in carrying out a titration.

5) Why should you first carry out a rough titration when carrying out a titration experiment?

6) Why shouldn't you use Universal indicator as an indicator in a titration?

7) Name two suitable indicators for a titration between an acid and an alkali,
   and state their colours when in acidic and alkaline solution.

8) What is a strong acid?

9) By what factor does the H^+ concentration increase for a decrease of 1 on the pH scale?

10) Explain the difference between a strong acid and a concentrated one.

11) Write a balanced equation for the reaction between hydrochloric acid and sodium carbonate.

<u>The Reactivity Series (p. 55)</u> ☑

12) Is zinc more or less reactive than iron?

13) What is the general word equation for the reaction of a metal with an acid?

14) Give the balanced equation for the reaction of calcium with water.

15) Will copper react with water?

<u>Reduction and Oxidation (p.56-57)</u> ☐

16) What product forms in the oxidation of magnesium by oxygen?

17) Explain how you decide whether a metal can be extracted from its oxide by reduction with carbon.

18) Why is gold found as itself in the earth?

19) In terms of electrons, give the definition of oxidation.

20) In a displacement reaction, does the metal atom get reduced or oxidised?

<u>Electrolysis (p.58-59)</u> ☑

21) During electrolysis, which electrode are the positive ions attracted to?

22) Why can ionic solids not undergo electrolysis?

23) Do ions get reduced or oxidised at the anode?

24) During the manufacture of aluminium from bauxite, which electrode is aluminium formed at?

25) In what situation will hydrogen gas be given out during
    the electrolysis of an aqueous solution of an ionic solid?

26) If halide ions are present in an aqueous solution of an ionic solid will oxygen gas be released?

27) What test could you use to determine if hydrogen gas has been produced in an electrolysis reaction?

Exothermic and Endothermic Reactions

Whenever chemical reactions occur, there are changes in <u>energy</u>. This means that when chemicals get together, things either hot up or cool right off. I'll give you a heads up — this page is a good 'un.

Energy is Moved Around in Chemical Reactions

1) Chemicals <u>store</u> a certain amount of energy — and <u>different chemicals</u> store <u>different amounts</u>.

2) If the <u>products</u> of a reaction store <u>more</u> energy than the <u>original reactants</u>, then they must have <u>taken in</u> the difference in energy between the products and reactants from the <u>surroundings</u> during the reaction.

3) But if they store <u>less</u>, then the <u>excess</u> energy was transferred <u>to the surroundings</u> during the reaction.

4) The <u>overall</u> amount of energy doesn't change. This is because energy is <u>conserved</u> in reactions — it can't be created or destroyed, only <u>moved around</u>. This means the amount of energy in the <u>universe</u> always stays the <u>same</u>.

In an Exothermic Reaction, Heat is Given Out

1) An <u>EXOTHERMIC</u> reaction is one which <u>transfers</u> energy to the <u>surroundings</u>, usually by <u>heating</u>. This is shown by a <u>rise in temperature</u>.

2) The best example of an exothermic reaction is <u>burning fuels</u> — also called <u>COMBUSTION</u>. This gives out a lot of energy — it's very exothermic.

3) <u>Neutralisation reactions</u> (acid + alkali) are also exothermic.

4) Many <u>oxidation reactions</u> are exothermic. For example, adding sodium to water <u>releases energy</u>, so it must be exothermic — see page 24. The reaction <u>releases energy</u> and the sodium moves about on the surface of the water as it is oxidised.

5) Exothermic reactions have lots of everyday uses. For example:

> • Some <u>hand warmers</u> use the exothermic oxidation of <u>iron</u> in air (with a salt solution catalyst) to <u>release energy</u>.
>
> • <u>Self heating cans</u> of hot chocolate and coffee also rely on <u>exothermic reactions</u> between chemicals in their bases.

In an Endothermic Reaction, Heat is Taken In

Physical processes can also take in or release energy. E.g. freezing is an exothermic process, melting is endothermic.

1) An <u>ENDOTHERMIC</u> reaction is one which <u>takes in</u> energy <u>from</u> the surroundings. This is shown by a <u>fall in temperature</u>.

2) Endothermic reactions are much <u>less common</u> than exothermic reactions, but they include:

• The reaction between <u>citric acid</u> and <u>sodium hydrogencarbonate</u>.

• <u>Thermal decomposition</u> — e.g. heating calcium carbonate causes it to decompose into calcium oxide (also called quicklime) and carbon dioxide:

$$\text{Calcium} \underset{\text{carbonate}}{\overline{}} CaCO_3 \; (+ \; \underline{HEAT}) \quad \rightarrow \quad CO_2 + CaO \underline{}\text{Quicklime}$$

3) Endothermic reactions also have everyday uses. For example:

> Endothermic reactions are used in some <u>sports injury packs</u> — the chemical reaction allows the pack to become <u>instantly cooler</u> without having to put it in the <u>freezer</u>.

Right, so burning gives out heat — really...

Remember, "exo-" = exit, "-thermic" = heat, so an exothermic reaction is one that gives out heat — and endothermic means just the opposite. To make sure you really understand these terms, try this question.

Q1   A student prepares a flask containing ethanoic acid and measures its temperature as 22.5 °C. He then adds dilute potassium hydroxide solution which is 21 °C. After 2 minutes the temperature of the reaction mixture is 28.5 °C. Is the reaction exothermic or endothermic?   [1 mark]

More Exothermic and Endothermic Reactions

Sometimes it's not enough to just know if a reaction is endothermic or exothermic. You may also need to know <u>how much</u> energy is absorbed or released — you can do experiments to find this out. Fun, fun, fun...

Energy Transfer can be Measured

PRACTICAL

1) You can measure the amount of <u>energy released</u> by a <u>chemical reaction</u> (in solution) by taking the <u>temperature of the reagents</u>, <u>mixing</u> them in a <u>polystyrene cup</u> and measuring the <u>temperature of the solution</u> at the <u>end</u> of the reaction. Easy.

2) The biggest <u>problem</u> with energy measurements is the amount of energy <u>lost to the surroundings</u>.

3) You can reduce it a bit by putting the polystyrene cup into a <u>beaker of cotton wool</u> to give <u>more insulation</u>, and putting a <u>lid</u> on the cup to reduce energy lost by <u>evaporation</u>.

4) This method works for <u>neutralisation</u> reactions or reactions between metals and acids, or carbonates and acids.

5) You can also use this method to investigate what effect different <u>variables</u> have on the <u>amount</u> of energy transferred — e.g. the <u>mass</u> or <u>concentration</u> of the reactants used.

6) Here's how you could test the effect of <u>acid concentration</u> on the energy released in a <u>neutralisation</u> reaction between hydrochloric acid (HCl) and sodium hydroxide (NaOH):

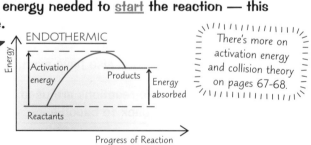

1) Put 25 cm³ of 0.25 mol/dm³ of hydrochloric acid and sodium hydroxide in <u>separate beakers</u>.
2) Place the beakers in a water bath set to 25 °C until they are both at the <u>same temperature</u> (25 °C).
3) Add the HCl followed by the NaOH to a polystyrene cup with a lid — as in the diagram above.
4) Take the temperature of the mixture <u>every 30 seconds</u>, and record the highest temperature.
5) <u>Repeat</u> steps 1-4 using 0.5 mol/dm³ and then 1 mol/dm³ of hydrochloric acid.

Reaction Profiles Show Energy Changes

Reaction profiles are sometimes called energy level diagrams.

<u>Reaction profiles</u> are diagrams that show the <u>relative energies</u> of the reactants and products in a reaction, and how the energy <u>changes</u> over the course of the reaction.

1) This shows an <u>exothermic reaction</u> — the products are at a <u>lower energy</u> than the reactants. The difference in <u>height</u> represents the overall energy change in the reaction (the energy given out) per mole.

2) The <u>initial rise</u> in energy represents the energy needed to <u>start the reaction</u>. This is the <u>activation energy</u> (E_a).

3) The activation energy is the <u>minimum amount</u> of energy the reactants need to <u>collide with each other</u> and <u>react</u>. The <u>greater</u> the activation energy, the <u>more</u> energy needed to <u>start</u> the reaction — this has to be <u>supplied</u>, e.g. by <u>heating</u> the reaction mixture.

1) This shows an <u>endothermic reaction</u> because the products are at a <u>higher energy</u> than the reactants.

2) The difference in <u>height</u> represents the overall energy change during the reaction (the energy <u>taken in</u>) per mole.

There's more on activation energy and collision theory on pages 67-68.

Energy transfer — make sure you take it all in...

Don't get confused by these diagrams. In an exothermic reaction the particles release energy to their surroundings — even though the reaction mixture gets warmer, the particles themselves have lost energy.

Q1 Here is the equation for the combustion of methane in air: $CH_{4(g)} + 2O_{2(g)} \rightarrow CO_{2(g)} + 2H_2O_{(g)}$
Draw a reaction profile for this reaction.
[3 marks]

Bond Energies

So you know that chemical reactions can take in or release energy — this page is about what <u>causes</u> these energy changes. Hint — it's all to do with <u>making</u> and <u>breaking</u> chemical bonds.

Energy Must Always be Supplied to Break Bonds

There's more on energy transfer on page 61.

1) During a chemical reaction, <u>old bonds are broken</u> and <u>new bonds are formed</u>.

2) Energy must be <u>supplied</u> to break existing bonds — so bond breaking is an <u>endothermic</u> process.

3) Energy is <u>released</u> when new bonds are formed — so bond formation is an <u>exothermic</u> process.

BOND BREAKING — <u>ENDOTHERMIC</u>

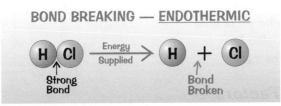

BOND FORMING — <u>EXOTHERMIC</u>

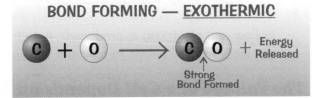

4) In <u>exothermic</u> reactions the energy <u>released</u> by forming bonds is <u>greater</u> than the energy used to <u>break</u> them. In <u>endothermic</u> reactions the energy <u>used</u> to break bonds is <u>greater</u> than the energy released by forming them.

Bond Energy Calculations — Need to be Practised

<u>Every</u> chemical bond has a particular <u>bond energy</u> associated with it. This <u>bond energy</u> varies slightly depending on the <u>compound</u> the bond occurs in.

You can use these <u>known bond energies</u> to calculate the <u>overall energy change</u> for a reaction. The overall energy change is the <u>sum</u> of the energies <u>needed</u> to break bonds in the reactants <u>minus</u> the energy <u>released</u> when the new bonds are formed in the products. You need to <u>practise</u> a few of these, but the basic idea is really very simple...

Bond forming

EXAMPLE: Using the bond energies given below, calculate the energy change for the reaction between H_2 and Cl_2 forming HCl:

$$H - H + Cl - Cl \longrightarrow \begin{array}{c} H - Cl \\ H - Cl \end{array}$$

The bond energies you need are: H–H: +436 kJ/mol; Cl–Cl: +242 kJ/mol; H–Cl: +431 kJ/mol.

1) Find the <u>energy required</u> to break the original bonds:
(1 × H–H) + (1 × Cl–Cl) = 436 kJ/mol + 242 kJ/mol = 678 kJ/mol

2) Find the <u>energy released</u> by forming the new bonds.
2 × H–Cl = 2 × 431 kJ/mol = 862 kJ/mol

3) Find the <u>overall energy change</u> for the reaction using this equation:
Overall energy change = energy required to break bonds − energy released by forming bonds
= 678 kJ/mol − 862 kJ/mol = −184 kJ/mol

You <u>can't compare</u> the overall energy changes of reactions unless you know the <u>numerical differences</u> in the bond energies.

Chlorine and bromine react with hydrogen in a similar way. <u>Br–Br</u> bonds are <u>weaker</u> than Cl–Cl bonds and <u>H–Br</u> bonds are <u>weaker</u> than H–Cl bonds. So <u>less energy</u> is needed to <u>break</u> the bonds in the reaction with bromine, but <u>less energy</u> is <u>released</u> when the new bonds form. So unless you know the <u>exact difference</u>, you can't say which reaction releases more energy.

A student and their bed — a bond that can never be broken...

This stuff might look hard at the moment, but with a bit of practice it's dead easy and it'll win you easy marks if you understand all the theory behind it. See how you get on with this question:

Q1 N_2 reacts with H_2 in the following reaction: $N_2 + 3H_2 \rightarrow 2NH_3$
The bond energies for these molecules are:
N≡N: 941 kJ/mol; H–H: 436 kJ/mol; N–H: 391 kJ/mol.
Calculate the overall energy change for this reaction

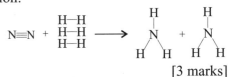

[3 marks]

Cells and Batteries

<u>Batteries</u> are dead useful for all sorts of things and, great news — now you can find out <u>how they work</u>.

Chemical Reactions in a Cell Produce Electricity

An <u>electrochemical cell</u> is a basic system made up of <u>two different electrodes</u> in contact with an <u>electrolyte</u>:

1) The two <u>electrodes</u> must be able to <u>conduct electricity</u> and so are usually metals.
2) The <u>electrolyte</u> is a liquid that contains <u>ions</u> which <u>react</u> with the electrodes.
3) The chemical reactions between the electrodes and the electrolyte set up a <u>charge difference</u> between the electrodes.
4) If the electrodes are then <u>connected</u> by a wire, the charge is able to flow and <u>electricity</u> is produced. A <u>voltmeter</u> can also be connected to the circuit to measure the <u>voltage</u> of the cell.

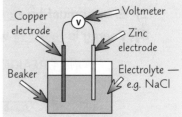

The Voltage of a Cell Depends on Many Factors

1) <u>Different</u> metals will <u>react differently</u> with the same electrolyte — this is what causes the <u>charge difference</u>, or the <u>voltage</u>, of the cell. So the <u>type of electrodes</u> used will affect the voltage of the cell.
2) The bigger the <u>difference</u> in <u>reactivity</u> of the electrodes, the <u>bigger</u> the <u>voltage</u> of the cell.
3) You can <u>predict</u> what the voltage of a cell might be from information about the voltages of other cells.

EXAMPLE: The voltages of two simple cells with the same electrolyte and different electrodes are shown in the table. If the metal used for Electrode A is less reactive than the other metal electrode, the voltage is positive and vice versa. Calculate the voltage of a cell where Electrode A is lead and Electrode B is tin.

Electrode A	Electrode B	Voltage (V)
Iron	Tin	−0.30
Iron	Lead	−0.31

The voltages of both cells are negative, so iron is more reactive than tin and lead. The voltage for the iron/lead cell is more negative than the iron/tin cell, so lead is less reactive than tin. The difference in voltage of these two cells is 0.01 V. So, for a cell where Electrode A is lead and Electrode B is tin, the voltage is **+0.01 V**.

4) The <u>electrolyte</u> used in a cell will also affect the size of the voltage since <u>different ions</u> in solution will react differently with the metal electrodes used.
5) A <u>battery</u> is formed by connecting two or more cells together in <u>series</u>. The voltages of the cells in the battery are <u>combined</u> so there is a <u>bigger</u> voltage overall.

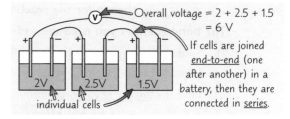

In Non-Rechargeable Batteries the Reactants Get Used Up

1) In some cells, the chemical reactions that happen at the electrodes are <u>irreversible</u>.
2) Over time the reacting particles — the ions in the electrolyte and the metal ions on the electrode — get <u>used up</u> and turned into the <u>products</u> of the reaction.
3) Once <u>any one</u> of the reactants is used up, the reaction <u>can't happen</u> and so <u>no electricity</u> is produced.
4) The products <u>can't</u> be turned back into the reactants, so the cell can't be <u>recharged</u>.

> <u>Non-rechargeable</u> batteries, e.g. <u>alkaline batteries</u>, contain cells which use irreversible reactions. Once <u>one</u> of the reactants is used up, they don't produce any more <u>charge</u> and you have to replace them.

5) In a <u>rechargeable</u> cell, the reaction can be <u>reversed</u> by connecting it to an <u>external electric current</u>.

I think I need a new battery for my brain after that...

Most so-called 'batteries' you use are probably cells. Confusing, but remember to use the right word in the exams.

Q1 The voltages of three cells, where one electrode is zinc and the other electrode changes each time are shown in the table. Zinc is less reactive than the other metals. Write the order of reactivity of the metals used from lowest to highest. Explain your answer. [3 marks]

Metal	1	2	3
Voltage (V)	4	2.5	3

Fuel Cells

We need <u>fuel</u> to move around — and I don't mean the eggs and bacon to get you out of bed on a Saturday...

Fuel Cells Use Fuel and Oxygen to Produce Electrical Energy

1) A <u>fuel cell</u> is an electrical cell that's supplied with a <u>fuel</u> and <u>oxygen</u> (or air) and uses <u>energy</u> from the reaction between them to produce electrical energy <u>efficiently</u>.

2) When the fuel enters the cell it becomes <u>oxidised</u> and sets up a <u>potential difference</u> within the cell.

3) There are a few <u>different types</u> of fuel cells, using different fuels and different electrolytes. One important example is the <u>hydrogen-oxygen fuel cell</u>.

4) This fuel cell combines hydrogen and oxygen to produce nice clean <u>water</u> and <u>release energy</u>.

Hydrogen-Oxygen Fuel Cells Involve a Redox Reaction

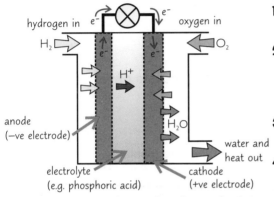

1) The electrolyte is often an <u>acid</u>, such as <u>phosphoric acid</u>. The electrodes are often porous carbon with a catalyst.

2) <u>Hydrogen</u> goes into the <u>anode compartment</u> and <u>oxygen</u> goes into the <u>cathode compartment</u>. Watch out — in electrolysis the anode is the positive electrode and the cathode is the negative one. When dealing with fuel cells, they're the other way round.

3) At the –ve electrode (the <u>anode</u>), hydrogen loses electrons to produce H^+ ions. This is <u>oxidation</u>.

4) <u>H</u>$^+$ ions in the electrolyte move to the <u>cathode</u> (+ve).

$$H_2 \rightarrow 2H^+ + 2e^-$$

These are the <u>half-equations</u> that show what's happening at each electrode.

5) At the +ve electrode (the <u>cathode</u>), <u>oxygen gains electrons</u> from the cathode and reacts with <u>H</u>$^+$ <u>ions</u> (from the acidic electrolyte) to make <u>water</u>. This is <u>reduction</u>.

6) The electrons flow through an <u>external circuit</u> from the anode to the cathode — this is the <u>electric current</u>.

7) The overall reaction is <u>hydrogen</u> plus <u>oxygen</u>, which gives water.

$$O_2 + 4H^+ + 4e^- \rightarrow 2H_2O$$

$$2H_2 + O_2 \rightarrow 2H_2O$$

There's reduction at the cathode and oxidation at the anode, so it's a redox reaction. See page 57 for more on redox reactions.

Hydrogen-Oxygen Fuel Cells Could be Used in Vehicles

<u>Conventional</u> fuels for vehicles (such as petrol) have a <u>finite supply</u> — they won't last forever, and they're very polluting. So vehicles that use <u>electrical energy</u> are becoming more and more popular. <u>Batteries</u> are one way of getting cleaner energy but <u>hydrogen-oxygen fuel cells</u> might be even better:

- Fuel cell vehicles don't produce as many <u>pollutants</u> as other fuels — no greenhouse gases, nitrogen oxides, sulfur dioxide or carbon monoxide. The only by-products are water and heat. <u>Electric vehicles</u> don't produce many pollutants either — but their <u>batteries</u> are more polluting to <u>dispose of</u> than fuel cells because they're made from <u>highly toxic</u> metal compounds.
- Batteries in electric vehicles are <u>rechargeable</u> but there's a limit to <u>how many times</u> they can be recharged before they need replacing. And batteries are <u>more expensive</u> to make than fuel cells.
- Batteries also <u>store less energy</u> than fuel cells and so would need to be recharged <u>more often</u> — which can take a <u>long time</u>.

However, there are still some <u>disadvantages</u> of using hydrogen fuel cells:

- Hydrogen is a <u>gas</u>, so it takes up loads more <u>space</u> to store than a rechargeable battery.
- Hydrogen is <u>explosive</u> when mixed with air so it's hard to store <u>safely</u>.
- The hydrogen fuel is often made either from <u>hydrocarbons</u> (from <u>fossil fuels</u>), or by <u>electrolysis</u> of water, which uses <u>electricity</u> (and that electricity has got to be generated somehow — usually from fossil fuels).

Fuel cells — they're simply electrifying...

Fuels cells could be really important for generating electricity cleanly — but there are some issues to sort out first.

Q1   Write the half equation for the reaction of oxygen in a hydrogen-oxygen fuel cell.   [2 marks]

Revision Questions for Topic 5

Right, let's see how much you can remember — don't worry though, you can flick back if you get stuck.

* Try these questions and <u>tick off each one</u> when you <u>get it right</u>.
* When you've done <u>all the questions</u> under a heading and are <u>completely happy</u> with it, tick it off.

Exothermic and Endothermic Reactions (p.61-62) ☑

1) In an exothermic reaction is heat transferred to or from the surroundings? ☑
2) Name two different types of reaction which are exothermic. ☑
3) Define what is meant by an endothermic reaction. ☑
4) Write down the equation for the thermal decomposition of calcium carbonate. ☑
5) What is the purpose of putting the reaction container into a beaker containing cotton wool during an experiment to investigate the temperature change of an exothermic reaction? ☑
6) Sketch an energy level diagram for an endothermic reaction. ☑
7) What is the activation energy of a reaction? ☑
8) Is the following statement true or false? In an endothermic reaction, the products of the reaction have more energy than the reactants. ☑

Bond Energies (p.63) ☑

9) For the following sentences, use either endothermic or exothermic to fill in the blanks:
   a) Bond breaking is an _____ process.
   b) Bond forming is an _____ process.
   c) In an _____ reaction, the energy released by forming bonds is greater than the energy used to break them. ☑
10) What three steps would you use to find the overall energy change in a reaction if you were given the known bond enthalpies for the bonds present in the reactants and products? ☐

Cells and Batteries (p.64) ☑

11) What is an electrolyte in an electrochemical cell? ☑
12) Give two factors that affect the voltage produced by an electrochemical cell. ☑
13) What is a battery? ☑
14) Explain why non-rechargeable batteries eventually lose their charge. ☑

Fuel Cells (p.65) ☐

15) What is a fuel cell? ☑
16) Name an electrolyte commonly used in hydrogen-oxygen fuel cells. ☑
17) In a hydrogen-oxygen fuel cell, which molecule becomes oxidised and which becomes reduced? ☑
18) Write down the overall equation for the reaction in hydrogen-oxygen fuel cells. ☑
19) Why is the reaction that takes place in a hydrogen-oxygen fuel cell described as a redox reaction? ☑
20) State 3 advantages of hydrogen-oxygen fuel cell powered cars over battery-powered electrical cars. ☑

Rates of Reaction

Rates of reaction are pretty <u>important</u>. In the <u>chemical industry</u>, the <u>faster</u> you make <u>chemicals</u>, the <u>faster</u> you make <u>money</u> (and the faster everyone gets to go home for tea).

Reactions Can Go at All Sorts of Different Rates

1) The rate of a chemical reaction is how fast the <u>reactants</u> are <u>changed</u> into <u>products</u>.

2) One of the <u>slowest</u> is the rusting of iron (it's not slow enough though — what about my little Mini).

3) Other <u>slow</u> reactions include <u>chemical weathering</u> — like acid rain damage to limestone buildings.

4) An example of a <u>moderate speed</u> reaction would be the metal <u>magnesium</u> reacting with an <u>acid</u> to produce a gentle stream of bubbles.

5) <u>Burning</u> is a <u>fast</u> reaction, but <u>explosions</u> are even <u>faster</u> and release a lot of gas. Explosive reactions are all over in a <u>fraction of a second</u>.

You Need to Understand Graphs for the Rate of Reaction

1) You can find the speed of a reaction by recording the amount of <u>product formed</u>, or the amount of <u>reactant used up</u> over <u>time</u> (see page 69).

2) The <u>steeper</u> the line on the graph, the <u>faster</u> the rate of reaction. <u>Over time</u> the line becomes <u>less steep</u> as the reactants are <u>used up</u>.

3) The <u>quickest reactions</u> have the <u>steepest</u> lines and become <u>flat</u> in the <u>least time</u>.

4) The plot below uses the amount of <u>product formed</u> over time to show how the <u>speed</u> of a particular reaction varies under <u>different conditions</u>.

> For more on the conditions that affect the rate of reaction — see next page.

- Graph 1 represents the <u>original reaction</u>.

- Graphs 2 and 3 represent the reaction taking place <u>quicker</u>, but with the <u>same initial amounts</u> of reactants. The slopes of the graphs are <u>steeper</u> than for graph 1.

- Graphs 1, 2 and 3 all converge at the <u>same level</u>, showing that they all produce the <u>same amount</u> of product although they take <u>different times</u> to produce it.

- Graph 4 shows <u>more product</u> and a <u>faster reaction</u>. This can only happen if <u>more reactant(s)</u> are added at the start.

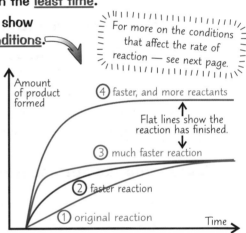

Particles Must Collide with Enough Energy in Order to React

Reaction rates are explained perfectly by <u>collision theory</u>. It's simple really. The <u>rate</u> of a chemical reaction depends on:

1) The <u>collision frequency</u> of reacting particles (how <u>often</u> they collide). The <u>more</u> collisions there are the <u>faster</u> the reaction is. E.g. doubling the frequency of collisions doubles the rate.

2) The energy <u>transferred</u> during a collision. Particles have to collide with <u>enough energy</u> for the collision to be successful.

> A successful collision is a collision that ends in the particles reacting to form products.

You might remember from page 62 that the <u>minimum</u> amount of energy that particles need to react is called the <u>activation energy</u>. Particles need this much energy to <u>break the bonds</u> in the reactants and start the reaction.

Factors that <u>increase</u> the <u>number</u> of collisions (so that a <u>greater proportion</u> of reacting particles collide) or the amount of <u>energy</u> particles collide with will <u>increase</u> the <u>rate</u> of the reaction (see next page for more).

Get a fast, furious reaction — tickle your teacher...

Collision theory's essential for understanding how different factors affect the rate of reaction — so make sure you understand it before moving on to the rest of Topic 6.

Q1   What is meant by the term activation energy?   [1 mark]

Factors Affecting Rates of Reaction

I'd ask you to <u>guess</u> what this page is about, but the <u>title</u> pretty much says it all really. Read on...

The Rate of Reaction Depends on Four Things

1) <u>Temperature</u>.
2) The <u>concentration</u> of a solution or the <u>pressure</u> of gas.
3) <u>Surface area</u> — this changes depending on the size of the lumps of a solid.
4) The presence of a <u>catalyst</u>.

More Collisions Increases the Rate of Reaction

All four methods of increasing the rate of a reaction can be explained in terms of increasing the <u>number</u> of <u>successful collisions</u> between the reacting particles:

Increasing the Temperature Increases the Rate

Cold   Hot

1) When the temperature is <u>increased</u>, the particles all move <u>faster</u>.
2) If they're moving faster, they're going to collide more <u>frequently</u>.
3) Also the faster they move the <u>more energy</u> they have, so <u>more</u> of the <u>collisions</u> will have <u>enough energy</u> to make the reaction happen.

Increasing the Concentration or Pressure Increases the Rate

1) If a solution is made more <u>concentrated</u>, it means there are <u>more particles</u> knocking about in the <u>same volume</u> of water (or other solvent).
2) Similarly, when the <u>pressure</u> of a gas is increased, it means that the <u>same number</u> of particles occupies a <u>smaller space</u>.
3) This makes <u>collisions</u> between the reactant particles <u>more frequent</u>.

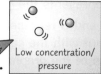
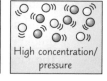
Low concentration/ pressure   High concentration/ pressure

Increasing the Surface Area Increases the Rate

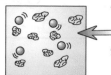

1) If one of the reactants is a <u>solid</u>, then breaking it up into <u>smaller pieces</u> will increase its <u>surface area to volume ratio</u>.
2) This means that for the <u>same volume</u> of the solid, the particles around it will have <u>more area</u> to work on — so there will be collisions <u>more frequently</u>.

Using a Catalyst Increases the Rate

1) A catalyst is a substance that <u>speeds up</u> a reaction, <u>without</u> being <u>used up</u> in the reaction itself. This means it's <u>not</u> part of the overall reaction <u>equation</u>.
2) <u>Different</u> catalysts are needed for different reactions, but they all work by <u>decreasing</u> the <u>activation energy</u> needed for the reaction to occur. They do this by providing an <u>alternative reaction pathway</u> with a <u>lower</u> activation energy.
3) Enzymes are <u>biological catalysts</u> — they catalyse reactions in <u>living things</u>.

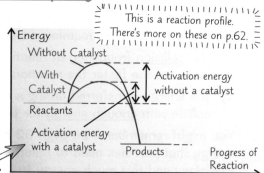
This is a reaction profile. There's more on these on p.62.

Increase your concentration — burn through that exam paper...

Catalysts are really useful — they don't get used up so you can use them over and over again. Brilliant.

Q1   For each of the following pairs of reactions, state which one would have the fastest rate (A or B) and why:
 a) A: A 2 g solid strip of magnesium with water.   B: 2 g of powdered magnesium with water.   [2 marks]
 b) A: 2 mol/dm^3 KOH with excess ethanoic acid.   B: 4 mol/dm^3 KOH with excess ethanoic acid. [2 marks]

Topic 6 — The Rate and Extent of Chemical Change

Measuring Rates of Reaction PRACTICAL

All this talk about rates of reactions is fine and dandy, but it's no good if you can't <u>measure</u> it.

Here Are Three Ways to Measure the Rate of a Reaction

The rate of a reaction can be observed either by how quickly the <u>reactants are used up</u> or how quickly the <u>products are formed</u>:

$$\text{Rate of Reaction} = \frac{\text{Amount of reactant used or amount of product formed}}{\text{Time}}$$

This is the mean rate of reaction. To find the rate of a reaction at a particular time, you'll need to plot a graph and find the gradient at that time (see page 71).

When the product or reactant is a <u>gas</u> you usually measure the amount in <u>cm³</u>. If it's a <u>solid</u>, then you use <u>grams (g)</u>. Time is often measured in <u>seconds (s)</u>. This means that the units for rate may be in <u>cm³/s</u> or in <u>g/s</u>. You can also measure the amount of product or reactant in <u>moles</u> — so the units of rate could also be <u>mol/s</u>. Here are <u>three different ways</u> of measuring the rate of a reaction:

A posh way of saying that the cloudiness of a solution changes is to say that its 'turbidity' changes.

1) Precipitation and Colour Change

1) You can record the <u>visual change</u> in a reaction if the initial solution is <u>transparent</u> and the product is a <u>precipitate</u> which <u>clouds</u> the solution (it becomes <u>opaque</u>).

2) You can observe a <u>mark</u> through the solution and measure how long it takes for it to <u>disappear</u> — the <u>faster</u> the mark disappears, the <u>quicker</u> the reaction.

3) If the reactants are <u>coloured</u> and the products are <u>colourless</u> (or vice versa), you can time how long it takes for the solution to <u>lose (or gain) its colour</u>.

4) The results are very <u>subjective</u> — <u>different people</u> might not agree over the <u>exact</u> point when the mark 'disappears' or the solution changes colour. Also, if you use this method, you can't plot a rate of reaction <u>graph</u> from the results.

2) Change in Mass (Usually Gas Given Off)

1) Measuring the speed of a reaction that <u>produces a gas</u> can be carried out using a <u>mass balance</u>.

2) As the gas is released, the mass <u>disappearing</u> is measured on the balance.

3) The <u>quicker</u> the reading on the balance <u>drops</u>, the <u>faster</u> the reaction.

4) If you take measurements at <u>regular intervals</u>, you can plot a rate of reaction <u>graph</u> and find the rate quite easily (see page 71 for more).

5) This is the <u>most accurate</u> of the three methods described on this page because the mass balance is very accurate. But it has the <u>disadvantage</u> of releasing the gas straight into the room.

3) The Volume of Gas Given Off

1) This involves the use of a <u>gas syringe</u> to measure the volume of gas <u>given off</u>.

2) The <u>more</u> gas given off during a given time interval, the <u>faster</u> the reaction.

3) Gas syringes usually give volumes accurate to the nearest <u>cm³</u>, so they're quite <u>accurate</u>. You can take measurements at <u>regular intervals</u> and plot a rate of reaction <u>graph</u> using this method too. You have to be quite careful though — if the reaction is too <u>vigorous</u>, you can easily blow the plunger out of the end of the syringe.

OK, have you got your stopwatch ready... *BANG!* — oh...

Make sure you've learnt the three different methods on this page, then have a go at this question:

Q1 The reaction between solid Na_2CO_3 and aqueous HCl releases CO_2 (a gas).
   a) Describe an experiment that would allow you to measure the rate of this reaction. [3 marks]
   b) Suggest units that would be appropriate for expressing the rate of this reaction. [1 mark]

Two Rates Experiments

Here's a lovely page on <u>practical investigations</u> into the effect of <u>concentration</u> on the rate of a reaction. It's particularly lovely because it's got <u>two</u> methods that you could use. Get your safety goggles on and let's go...

Magnesium and HCl React to Produce H₂ Gas

1) Start by adding a set volume of <u>dilute hydrochloric acid</u> to a <u>conical flask</u> and carefully place on a <u>mass balance</u>.

2) Now add some <u>magnesium ribbon</u> to the acid and quickly <u>plug</u> the flask with <u>cotton wool</u>.

3) Start the <u>stopwatch</u> and record the <u>mass</u> on the balance. Take readings of the mass at <u>regular intervals</u>.

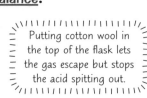
Putting cotton wool in the top of the flask lets the gas escape but stops the acid spitting out.

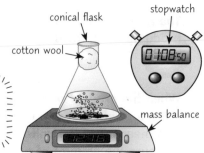
conical flask
stopwatch
cotton wool
mass balance

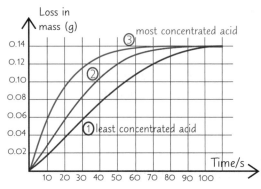

4) Plot the results in a table and work out the <u>mass lost</u> for each reading. Now you can plot a <u>graph</u> with <u>time</u> on the x-axis and <u>loss of mass</u> on the y-axis.

5) Repeat with <u>more concentrated</u> acid solutions. Variables such as the <u>amount</u> of magnesium ribbon and the <u>volume</u> of acid used should be kept the same each time — only change the acid's concentration. This is to make your experiment a <u>fair test</u> — see p.5.

6) The three graphs show that a <u>higher concentration</u> of acid gives a <u>faster rate of reaction</u>.

You could also measure the gas released using a gas syringe, as on the previous page.

Sodium Thiosulfate and HCl Produce a Cloudy Precipitate

1) These two chemicals are both <u>clear solutions</u>. They react together to form a <u>yellow precipitate</u> of <u>sulfur</u>.

2) Start by adding a set volume of <u>dilute sodium thiosulfate</u> to a conical flask.

3) Place the flask on a piece of paper with a <u>black cross</u> drawn on it. Add some <u>dilute HCl</u> to the flask and start the stopwatch.

4) Now watch the black cross <u>disappear</u> through the <u>cloudy sulfur</u> and <u>time</u> how long it takes to go.

5) The reaction can be <u>repeated</u> with solutions of either reactant at <u>different concentrations</u>. (Only change the concentration of <u>one reactant</u> at a time though). The <u>depth</u> of the liquid must be kept the <u>same</u> each time.

6) These results show the effect of <u>increasing</u> the <u>concentration</u> of <u>HCl</u> on the rate of reaction, when added to an excess of sodium thiosulfate.

This reaction releases sulfur dioxide, so the experiment should be carried out in a well-ventilated place.

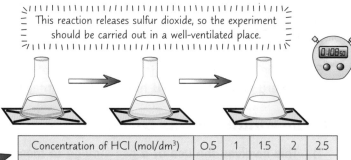

Concentration of HCl (mol/dm³)	0.5	1	1.5	2	2.5
Time taken for mark to disappear (s)	193	184	178	171	164

7) The <u>higher</u> the concentration, the <u>quicker</u> the reaction and therefore the <u>less time</u> it takes for the mark to disappear.

Although you could draw a graph of concentration against 1/time which will give you an approximate rate.

8) One sad thing about this reaction is that it <u>doesn't</u> give a set of <u>graphs</u>. Well I think it's sad. All you get is a set of <u>readings</u> of how long it took till the mark disappeared for each concentration. Boring.

Bubbling acid, sulfurous clouds — proper witchcraft this is...

You should learn the methods involved in these experiments — but remember, other reactions can also be used to investigate the four factors that affect rate. You might see different experiments in your exams, or the same ones but measuring a different factor — so watch out.

Q1   A student carried out an experiment investigating the effect of changing the HCl concentration on the rate of reaction between HCl and Mg. State two factors that he should have kept constant.   [2 marks]

Topic 6 — The Rate and Extent of Chemical Change

Finding Reaction Rates from Graphs

You might remember a bit about how to <u>interpret</u> graphs on reaction rate from page 67 — well this page shows you how to use them to <u>calculate</u> rates.

You can Calculate the Mean Reaction Rate from a Graph

1) Remember, a rate of reaction graph shows the amount of <u>product formed</u> or amount of <u>reactant used up</u> on the <u>y-axis</u> and <u>time</u> on the <u>x-axis</u>.

2) So to find the <u>mean rate</u> for the <u>whole reaction</u>, you just work out the <u>overall change</u> in the y-value and then <u>divide this</u> by the <u>total time taken</u> for the reaction.

3) You can also use the graph to find the <u>mean rate</u> of reaction between <u>any two points</u> in time:

 **EXAMPLE:**

The graph shows the volume of gas released by a reaction, measured at regular intervals. Find the mean rate of reaction between 20 s and 40 s.

Mean rate of reaction = change in y ÷ change in x
$$= (19 \text{ cm}^3 - 15 \text{ cm}^3) \div 20 \text{ s}.$$
$$= 0.2 \text{ cm}^3/\text{s}$$

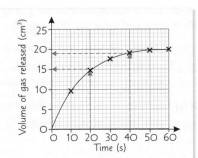

If you're asked to find the mean rate of reaction for the whole reaction, remember that the reaction finishes as soon as the line on the graph goes flat.

Draw a Tangent to Find the Reaction Rate at a Particular Point

If you want to find the <u>rate</u> of the reaction at a particular point in time, you need to find the <u>gradient</u> (slope) of the curve at that point. The easiest way to do this is to draw a <u>tangent</u> to the curve — a straight line that touches the curve at one point and doesn't cross it. You then work out the <u>gradient of the tangent</u>. It's simpler than it sounds, honest...

EXAMPLE: The graph below shows the mass of reactant used up measured at regular intervals during a chemical reaction. What is the rate of reaction at 3 minutes?

1) Position a <u>ruler</u> on the graph at the point where you want to know the rate — here it's <u>3 minutes</u>.

2) Adjust the ruler until the <u>space</u> between the ruler and the curve is <u>equal</u> on <u>both sides</u> of the point.

3) Draw a line along the ruler to make the <u>tangent</u>. Extend the line <u>right</u> <u>across</u> the graph.

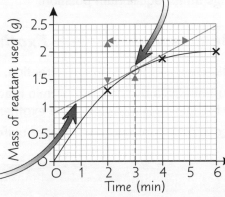

4) Pick <u>two points</u> on the line that are easy to read. Use them to calculate the <u>gradient</u> of the tangent in order to find the <u>rate</u>:

gradient = change in y ÷ change in x
$$= (2.2 - 1.4) \div (5.0 - 2.0)$$
$$= 0.8 \div 3.0$$
$$= 0.27$$

So, the rate of reaction at 3 minutes was 0.27 g/min.

Calculate your reaction to this page. Boredom? How dare you...

There's only one way to learn this stuff properly — practise. So you'd better get going with this question.

Q1 Calcium carbonate powder was added to a conical flask containing dilute HCl. CO_2 was produced and collected in a gas syringe. The volume of gas released was recorded at 10 second intervals in the following table:

Time (s)	10	20	30	40	50	60
Volume of CO_2 (cm³)	24	32	36	38	39	40

a) Plot these results on a graph and draw a line of best fit. [3 marks]
b) Find the rate of the reaction at time = 25 s. [4 marks]

Topic 6 — The Rate and Extent of Chemical Change

Reversible Reactions

Some reactions can go <u>backwards</u>. Honestly, that's all you need...

Reversible Reactions *Will Reach Equilibrium*

The '⇌' shows the reaction goes both ways.

This equation shows a <u>reversible reaction</u> — the <u>products</u> (C and D) can react to form the <u>reactants</u> (A and B) again:

$$A + B \rightleftharpoons C + D$$

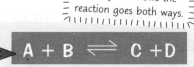

Forward Reaction

Same rate at equilibrium

Backward Reaction

1) As the <u>reactants</u> react, their concentrations <u>fall</u> — so the <u>forward reaction</u> will <u>slow down</u> (see page 68). But as more and more <u>products</u> are made and their concentrations <u>rise</u>, the <u>backward reaction</u> will <u>speed up</u>.

2) After a while the forward reaction will be going at <u>exactly the same rate</u> as the backward one — the system is at <u>equilibrium</u>.

3) At equilibrium, <u>both</u> reactions are still happening, but there's <u>no overall effect</u> (it's a dynamic equilibrium). This means the <u>concentrations</u> of reactants and products have reached a balance and <u>won't change</u>.

4) Equilibrium is only reached if the reversible reaction takes place in a '<u>closed system</u>'. A <u>closed system</u> just means that <u>none</u> of the reactants or products can <u>escape</u> and nothing else can get <u>in</u>.

The Position of Equilibrium *Can be on the Right or the Left*

1) When a reaction's at equilibrium it <u>doesn't</u> mean the amounts of reactants and products are <u>equal</u>.

2) If the equilibrium <u>lies to the right</u>, the concentration of <u>products</u> is <u>greater</u> than that of the reactants.

3) If the equilibrium <u>lies to the left</u>, the concentration of <u>reactants</u> is <u>greater</u> than that of the products.

4) The <u>position of equilibrium</u> depends on the following <u>conditions</u> (as well as the reaction itself):

- the <u>temperature</u>,
- the <u>pressure</u> (this only affects equilibria involving gases),
- the <u>concentration</u> of the reactants and products.

E.g. ammonium chloride ⇌ ammonia + hydrogen chloride
<u>Heating</u> this reaction moves the equilibrium to the <u>right</u> (more ammonia and hydrogen chloride) and <u>cooling</u> it moves it to the <u>left</u> (more ammonium chloride).

The next page tells you why these things affect equilibrium position.

Reversible Reactions *Can Be Endothermic and Exothermic*

1) In reversible reactions, if the reaction is <u>endothermic</u> in one direction, it will be <u>exothermic</u> in the other.

2) The energy transferred <u>from</u> the surroundings by the endothermic reaction is <u>equal to</u> the energy transferred <u>to</u> the surroundings during the exothermic reaction.

See page 61 for more on endothermic and exothermic reactions.

3) A good example is the <u>thermal decomposition</u> of hydrated copper sulfate:

'Anhydrous' just means 'without water', and 'hydrated' means 'with water'.

endothermic
hydrated copper sulfate ⇌ anhydrous copper sulfate + water
exothermic

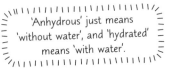

If you <u>heat blue hydrated</u> copper(II) sulfate crystals, it drives the water off and leaves <u>white anhydrous</u> copper(II) sulfate powder. This is <u>endothermic</u>.

If you then <u>add</u> a couple of drops of <u>water</u> to the <u>white powder</u> you get the <u>blue crystals</u> back again. This is <u>exothermic</u>.

*Dynamic equilibrium — lots of activity, but not to any great effect.**

Make sure you understand everything on this page before you move on to the next one. Trust me, it'll help.

Q1   What does it mean if a system is at equilibrium?   [1 mark]

* Much like the England football team.

Le Chatelier's Principle

Reversible reactions don't like being messed around — so if you change something, the system will respond to undo the change. Sneaky.

Reversible Reactions Try to Counteract Changes...

1) Le Chatelier's Principle is the idea that if you change the conditions of a reversible reaction at equilibrium, the system will try to counteract that change.

2) It can be used to predict the effect of any changes you make to a reaction system.

...Such as Changes to the Temperature...

1) All reactions are exothermic in one direction and endothermic in the other (see previous page).

2) If you decrease the temperature, the equilibrium will move in the exothermic direction to produce more heat. This means you'll get more products for the exothermic reaction and fewer products for the endothermic reaction.

3) If you raise the temperature, the equilibrium will move in the endothermic direction to try and decrease it. You'll now get more products for the endothermic reaction and fewer products for the exothermic reaction.

> $N_2 + 3H_2 \rightleftharpoons 2NH_3$
>
> Here the forward reaction is exothermic — a decrease in temperature moves equilibrium to the right (more NH_3).

...Pressure...

1) Changing the pressure only affects an equilibrium involving gases.

2) If you increase the pressure, the equilibrium tries to reduce it — it moves in the direction where there are fewer molecules of gas.

3) If you decrease the pressure, the equilibrium tries to increase it — it moves in the direction where there are more molecules of gas.

4) You can use the balanced symbol equation for a reaction to see which side has more molecules of gas.

> $N_2 + 3H_2 \rightleftharpoons 2NH_3$
>
> There are 4 moles on the left (1 of N_2 and 3 of H_2) but only 2 on the right. So, if you increase the pressure, the equilibrium shifts to the right (more NH_3).

...or Concentration

1) If you change the concentration of either the reactants or the products, the system will no longer be at equilibrium.

2) So the system responds to bring itself back to equilibrium again.

3) If you increase the concentration of the reactants the system tries to decrease it by making more products.

4) If you decrease the concentration of products the system tries to increase it again by reducing the amount of reactants.

> $N_2 + 3H_2 \rightleftharpoons 2NH_3$
>
> If more N_2 or H_2 is added, the forward reaction increases to produce more NH_3.

An equilibrium is like a particularly stubborn mule...

It's good science this stuff. You do one thing, and the reaction does the other. On the face of it, that sounds like it'd be pretty annoying, but in reality it's what gives you control of what happens in a reversible reaction. And in industry, control is what makes the whole shebang profitable. Mmmm... Money.

Q1 For the following reactions, state the effect of an increase in pressure on the amount of products at equilibrium.

a) $N_2O_{4(g)} \rightleftharpoons 2NO_{2(g)}$ [1 mark]

b) $ClNO_{2(g)} + NO_{(g)} \rightleftharpoons NO_{2(g)} + ClNO_{(g)}$ [1 mark]

c) $2CO_{(g)} + O_{2(g)} \rightleftharpoons 2CO_{2(g)}$ [1 mark]

Revision Questions for Topic 6

We'll you've almost made it — you're just one more page away from a lovely cup of tea and a biscuit...

- Try these questions and <u>tick off each one</u> when you <u>get it right</u>.
- When you've done <u>all the questions</u> under a heading and are <u>completely happy</u> with it, tick it off.

Rates of Reaction and Factors Affecting Them (p.67-68) ☑

1) On a rate of reaction graph, what does the line getting steeper show? ☑
2) What does a flat line on a graph of amount of products against time show? ☑
3) What two factors relating to the collisions between particles influence the rate of a reaction? ☑
4) What are the four factors that affect the rate of a chemical reaction? ☑
5) Why does increasing the temperature of a reaction mixture increase the rate of a reaction? ☑
6) Other than increasing the temperature, describe two ways of increasing the rate of reaction between a solution and a solid. ☑
7) What is a catalyst? ☑
8) How does a catalyst increase the rate of a reaction? ☑

Measuring and Calculating Rates of Reaction (p.69-71) ☑

9) State the equation that could be used to calculate the mean rate of a reaction. ☑
10) Give three possible units for the rate of a chemical reaction. ☑
11) How would you measure the rate of a reaction between two clear solutions, in which the product formed was a precipitate? ☑
12) Explain why measuring a mass change during a reaction is an accurate method of measuring rate. ☑
13) Describe how you could investigate the effect of increasing HCl concentration on the rate of reaction between HCl and Mg. ☑
14) Describe how you could use a graph to find the mean rate of a reaction between two points in time. ☑
15) What is a tangent? ☑
16) How would you use a tangent to find the gradient of a curve at a particular point? ☑

Reversible Reactions and Le Chatelier's Principle (p.72-73) ☑

17) Which one of the following statements is true?
  a) In a reaction at equilibrium, there is the same amount of products as reactants.
  b) If the forward reaction in a reversible reaction is exothermic, then the reverse reaction is endothermic.
  c) If the equilibrium of a system lies to the right, then the concentration of products is less than the concentration of reactants. ☐
18) What effect will decreasing the temperature have on a reversible reaction in which the forward reaction is exothermic? ☑
19) How can you predict the effect of changing the pressure of a gaseous reaction? ☑
20) According to Le Chatelier's Principle, what will the effect of decreasing the concentration of the products for the forward reaction have on a reversible reaction? ☑

Hydrocarbons

Organic chemistry is about compounds that contain <u>carbon</u>. <u>Hydrocarbons</u> are the simplest organic compounds. As you're about to discover, the <u>properties</u> of hydrocarbons make them really useful.

Hydrocarbons Only Contain Hydrogen and Carbon Atoms

A hydrocarbon is any compound that is formed from <u>carbon and hydrogen atoms only</u>.
So $C_{10}H_{22}$ (decane, an alkane) is a hydrocarbon, but $CH_3COOC_3H_7$ (an ester) is <u>not</u> — it contains oxygen.

Alkanes Have All C–C Single Bonds

1) <u>Alkanes</u> are the simplest type of hydrocarbon you can get. They have the general formula C_nH_{2n+2}.

2) The alkanes are a <u>homologous series</u> — a group of organic compounds that react in a similar way.

3) Alkanes are <u>saturated compounds</u> — each carbon atom forms four single covalent bonds.

4) The first four alkanes are <u>methane</u>, <u>ethane</u>, <u>propane</u> and <u>butane</u>.

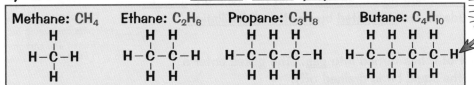

A drawing showing all the atoms and bonds in a molecule is called a displayed formula.

Alkane, Al saw, Al conquered.

Give it a rest, Alan!

Hydrocarbon Properties Change as the Chain Gets Longer

As the <u>length</u> of the carbon chain changes, the <u>properties</u> of the hydrocarbon change.

1) The <u>shorter</u> the carbon chain, the <u>more runny</u> a hydrocarbon is — that is, the <u>less viscous</u> (gloopy) it is.

2) Hydrocarbons with shorter carbon chains are also <u>more volatile</u>, i.e. they have lower boiling points.

3) Also, the <u>shorter</u> the carbon chain, the more <u>flammable</u> (easier to ignite) the hydrocarbon is.

4) The <u>properties</u> of hydrocarbons affect how they're used for fuels. E.g. <u>short chain</u> hydrocarbons with <u>lower</u> boiling points are used as 'bottled gases' — stored <u>under pressure</u> as <u>liquids</u> in bottles.

Complete Combustion Occurs When There's Plenty of Oxygen

1) The <u>complete combustion</u> of any hydrocarbon in oxygen releases lots of energy. The only waste products are <u>carbon dioxide</u> and <u>water</u> vapour.

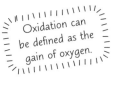

Oxidation can be defined as the gain of oxygen.

$$\text{hydrocarbon} + \text{oxygen} \rightarrow \text{carbon dioxide} + \text{water} \quad (+ \text{ energy})$$

2) During combustion, both carbon and hydrogen from the hydrocarbon are <u>oxidised</u>.

3) Hydrocarbons are used as <u>fuels</u> due to the <u>amount of energy</u> released when they combust completely.

4) You need to be able to give a <u>balanced symbol equation</u> for the <u>complete combustion</u> of a simple hydrocarbon fuel when you're given its <u>molecular formula</u>. It's pretty easy — here's an example:

EXAMPLE: Write a balanced equation for the complete combustion of methane (CH_4).

See p.15 for more on balancing equations.

1) On the <u>left hand side</u>, there's <u>one</u> carbon atom, so only <u>one</u> molecule of CO_2 is needed to balance this.

$$CH_4 + ?O_2 \rightarrow CO_2 + ?H_2O$$

2) On the <u>left hand side</u>, there are <u>four</u> hydrogen atoms, so <u>two</u> water molecules are needed to balance them.

$$CH_4 + ?O_2 \rightarrow CO_2 + 2H_2O$$

3) There are <u>four</u> oxygen atoms on the <u>right hand side</u> of the equation. <u>Two</u> oxygen molecules are needed on the left to balance them.

$$CH_4 + 2O_2 \rightarrow CO_2 + 2H_2O$$

The name's bond — single covalent bond...

So hydrocarbons only contain two ingredients — carbon and hydrogen. Jamie Oliver would not be happy.

Q1   A student has two alkanes, C_5H_{12} and $C_{10}H_{22}$. Compare the following properties of the alkanes:
    a) viscosity   b) boiling point   c) flammability   [3 marks]

Q2   Write a balanced symbol equation for the complete combustion of propane, C_3H_8.   [2 marks]

Fractional Distillation

Crude oil can be used to make loads of useful things, such as fuels. But you can't just put crude oil in your car. First, the different hydrocarbons have to be separated. That's where fractional distillation comes in.

Crude Oil is Made Over a Long Period of Time

1) Crude oil is a fossil fuel. It's formed from the remains of plants and animals, mainly plankton, that died millions of years ago and were buried in mud. Over millions of years, with high temperature and pressure, the remains turn to crude oil, which can be drilled up from the rocks where it's found.

2) Fossil fuels like coal, oil and gas are called non-renewable fuels as they take so long to make that they're being used up much faster than they're being formed. They're finite resources (see p.99) — one day they'll run out.

Fractional Distillation can be Used to Separate Hydrocarbon Fractions

Crude oil is a mixture of lots of different hydrocarbons, most of which are alkanes. The different compounds in crude oil are separated by fractional distillation.

Hydrocarbons are molecules containing only hydrogen and carbon.

Here's how it works:

1) The oil is heated until most of it has turned into gas. The gases enter a fractionating column (and the liquid bit is drained off).

2) In the column there's a temperature gradient (it's hot at the bottom and gets cooler as you go up).

3) The longer hydrocarbons have high boiling points. They condense back into liquids and drain out of the column early on, when they're near the bottom. The shorter hydrocarbons have lower boiling points. They condense and drain out much later on, near to the top of the column where it's cooler.

4) You end up with the crude oil mixture separated out into different fractions. Each fraction contains a mixture of hydrocarbons that all contain a similar number of carbon atoms, so have similar boiling points.

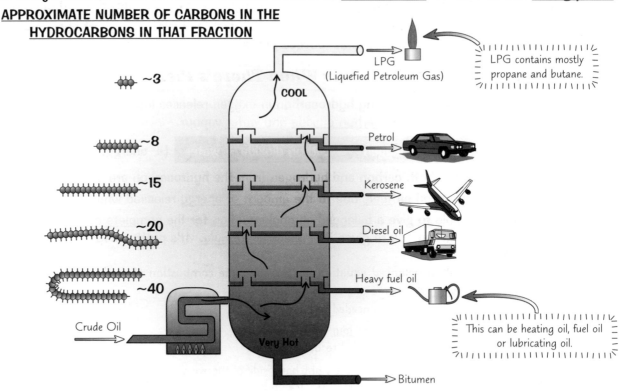

APPROXIMATE NUMBER OF CARBONS IN THE
HYDROCARBONS IN THAT FRACTION

~3

~8

~15

~20

~40

Crude Oil

COOL

Very Hot

LPG
(Liquefied Petroleum Gas)

LPG contains mostly propane and butane.

Petrol

Kerosene

Diesel oil

Heavy fuel oil

This can be heating oil, fuel oil or lubricating oil.

Bitumen

How much petrol is there in crude oil? Just a fraction...

Make sure you understand how fractional distillation works — it might just save your life... OK, maybe not.

Q1 Petrol drains further up a fractionating column than diesel. What does this suggest about the boiling points of the hydrocarbons which make up petrol compared to those in diesel? [1 mark]

Q2 Describe the temperature gradient in a fractionating column used for fractional distillation. [1 mark]

Uses and Cracking of Crude Oil

Crude oil has fuelled <u>modern civilisation</u> — it would be a very different world if we hadn't discovered oil.

Crude Oil has Various Uses Important in Modern Life

1) <u>Oil</u> provides the <u>fuel</u> for most modern <u>transport</u> — cars, trains, planes, the lot. Diesel oil, kerosene, heavy fuel oil and LPG (liquid petroleum gas) all come from crude oil.

2) The <u>petrochemical industry</u> uses some of the hydrocarbons from crude oil as a <u>feedstock</u> to make <u>new compounds</u> for use in things like <u>polymers</u>, <u>solvents</u>, <u>lubricants</u>, and <u>detergents</u>.

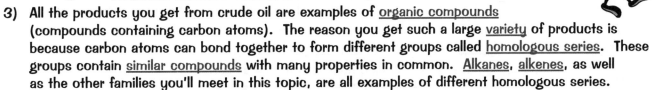

3) All the products you get from crude oil are examples of <u>organic compounds</u> (compounds containing carbon atoms). The reason you get such a large <u>variety</u> of products is because carbon atoms can bond together to form different groups called <u>homologous series</u>. These groups contain <u>similar compounds</u> with many properties in common. <u>Alkanes</u>, <u>alkenes</u>, as well as the other families you'll meet in this topic, are all examples of different homologous series.

Cracking Means Splitting Up Long-Chain Hydrocarbons

1) <u>Short-chain hydrocarbons</u> are flammable so make good fuels and are in high demand. However, <u>long-chain hydrocarbons</u> form <u>thick gloopy liquids</u> like <u>tar</u> which aren't all that useful, so...

2) ...a lot of the longer alkane molecules produced from <u>fractional distillation</u> are <u>turned</u> into <u>smaller</u>, <u>more useful</u> ones by a process called <u>cracking</u>.

3) As well as alkanes, cracking also produces another type of hydrocarbon called <u>alkenes</u>. Alkenes are used as a <u>starting material</u> when making lots of other compounds and can be used to make polymers (see p.80).

4) Some of the products of cracking are useful as <u>fuels</u>, e.g. petrol for cars and paraffin for jet fuel.

There are Different Methods of Cracking

1) <u>Cracking</u> is a <u>thermal decomposition</u> reaction — <u>breaking molecules down</u> by <u>heating</u> them.

2) The first step is to <u>heat</u> long-chain hydrocarbons to <u>vaporise</u> them (turn them into a gas).

3) Then the <u>vapour</u> is passed over a <u>hot</u> powdered aluminium oxide <u>catalyst</u>.

4) The <u>long-chain</u> molecules <u>split apart</u> on the <u>surface</u> of the specks of catalyst — this is <u>catalytic cracking</u>.

5) You can also crack hydrocarbons if you vaporise them, mix them with <u>steam</u> and then <u>heat</u> them to a very high temperature. This is known as <u>steam cracking</u>.

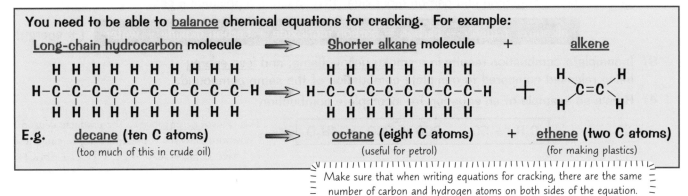

This page is tough — better get cracking...

We use lots of oil — we're dependent on it for loads of things. So we could be in a proper pickle when it runs out. Just like you could be in a pickle if you don't revise this page. See what I did there? Ahaha...

Q1   Pentane, C_5H_{12}, can be cracked into ethene, C_2H_4, and one other hydrocarbon.
        Give the formula of the other hydrocarbon.

[1 mark]

Alkenes

Alkenes are <u>unsaturated</u> because they have a <u>double</u> carbon-carbon bond. They're <u>hydrocarbons</u>, and their names sound like the alkanes on p.75. Don't mix them up, or you'll be the joke of the examiners' tea room...

Alkenes Have a C=C Double Bond

1) Alkenes are hydrocarbons which have a <u>double bond</u> between two of the <u>carbon</u> atoms in their chain.

2) The C=C double bond means that alkenes have <u>two fewer</u> hydrogens compared with alkanes containing the <u>same number</u> of carbon atoms. This makes them <u>unsaturated</u>.

3) The C=C double bond can open up to make a <u>single bond</u>, allowing the two carbon atoms to bond with <u>other atoms</u> (see the next page). This makes alkenes <u>reactive</u> — far more reactive than <u>alkanes</u>.

4) The first four alkenes are <u>ethene</u> (with two carbon atoms), <u>propene</u> (three Cs), <u>butene</u> (four Cs) and <u>pentene</u> (five Cs).

5) Straight-chain <u>alkenes</u> have twice as many hydrogen atoms as carbon:

General formula for alkenes = C_nH_{2n}

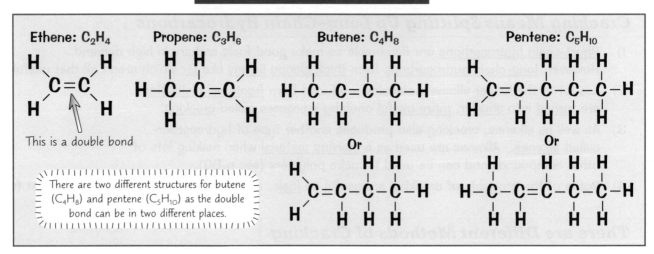

Alkenes Burn With a Smoky Flame

1) In a large amount of oxygen, alkenes <u>combust completely</u> to produce only water and carbon dioxide (see p.75).

2) However, there isn't enough oxygen in the air for this, so when you burn them they tend to undergo <u>incomplete combustion</u>. Carbon dioxide and water are still produced, but you can also get <u>carbon</u> and <u>carbon monoxide</u> (CO) which is a poisonous gas.

alkene + oxygen → carbon + carbon monoxide + carbon dioxide + water   (+ energy)

3) Incomplete combustion results in a <u>smoky yellow flame</u>, and <u>less energy</u> being released compared to complete combustion of the same compound.

4) Here's an example of an <u>equation</u> for incomplete combustion:

$C_4H_8 + 5O_2 \rightarrow 2CO + 2CO_2 + 4H_2O$

This is just <u>one possibility</u>. The products depend on how much oxygen is present. E.g. you could also have: $C_4H_8 + 3O_2 \rightarrow 2C + 2CO + 4H_2O$ — but the equation has to be <u>balanced</u>.

I hope you alkene to learn this page...

Don't get alkenes confused with alkanes — that letter 'e' makes all the difference. Alkenes have a C=C bond, alkanes don't. The first part of both their names tells you how many carbon atoms they have.

Q1   Give the chemical formula for the alkene that contains eight carbon atoms.   [1 mark]

Q2   Name two products which are produced during incomplete combustion which aren't produced during complete combustion.   [2 marks]

Reactions of Alkenes

Alkenes <u>react</u> with lots of compounds, which is great. Unless you have to learn the reactions that is...

Alkenes React via Addition Reactions

1) A <u>functional group</u> is a <u>group of atoms</u> in a molecule that determine <u>how</u> that molecule typically <u>reacts</u>.

2) All <u>alkenes</u> have the functional group 'C=C', so they all react in <u>similar ways</u>. So you can suggest the products of a reaction based on your knowledge of how alkenes react <u>in general</u>.

3) Most of the time, alkenes react via <u>addition reactions</u>. The carbon-carbon double bond will <u>open</u> up to leave a <u>single bond</u> and a new atom is added to each carbon:

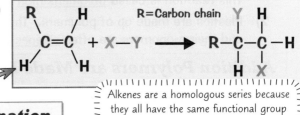

Alkenes are a homologous series because they all have the same functional group and react in similar ways.

Addition of Hydrogen is Known as Hydrogenation

<u>Hydrogen</u> can <u>react</u> with the <u>double-bonded</u> carbons to <u>open</u> up the double bond and form the equivalent, saturated, alkane.

The alkene is reacted with hydrogen in the presence of a <u>catalyst</u>:

Steam can React with Alkenes to Form Alcohols

1) When alkenes react with <u>steam</u>, <u>water</u> is added across the double bond and an <u>alcohol</u> is formed.

2) For example, <u>ethanol</u> can be made by mixing <u>ethene</u> with steam and then passing it over a <u>catalyst</u>:

3) The conversion of ethene to ethanol is one way of making ethanol <u>industrially</u>. After the reaction has taken place, the reaction mixture is passed from the reactor into a condenser. Ethanol and water have a <u>higher</u> boiling point than ethene, so both <u>condense</u> whilst any <u>unreacted ethene</u> gas is <u>recycled</u> back into the reactor. The alcohol can then be <u>purified</u> from the mixture by <u>fractional distillation</u>.

Have a look at p.81 for more on alcohols

Halogens can React with Alkenes

1) Alkenes will also react in <u>addition reactions</u> with <u>halogens</u> such as bromine, chlorine and iodine. The molecules formed are saturated, with the C=C carbons each becoming bonded to a halogen atom.

2) For example, bromine and ethene react together to form <u>dibromoethane</u>:

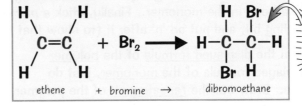

ethene + bromine → dibromoethane

There are two bromine atoms so it's called <u>dibromoethane</u>.

This reaction is the same for Cl_2 or I_2 except the halogen added is different.

The <u>addition</u> of bromine to a double bond can be used to test for <u>alkenes</u>:

1) When orange <u>bromine water</u> is added to a <u>saturated compound</u>, like an <u>alkane</u>, no reaction will happen and it'll stay <u>bright orange</u>.

2) If it's added to an <u>alkene</u> the <u>bromine</u> will add <u>across</u> the double bond, making a <u>colourless</u> dibromo-compound — so the bromine water is decolourised.

bromine water + an alkene → SHAKE → solution goes colourless

Double the carbon bonds, double the fun...

These reactions aren't too bad to get your head around. They're as easy as saying 'diiodoethane'...

Q1 Propene reacts with hydrogen in the presence of a nickel catalyst at 60 °C. Give the displayed formula of the product of this reaction. [1 mark]

Q2 State what colour change occurs when butene, C_4H_8, reacts with bromine water. [1 mark]

Addition Polymers

Polymers are made up of lots of the same molecule joined together in one long chain. They're what make up plastics. They have lots of weird and wonderful properties which make them darn useful to modern society.

Plastics are Made Up of Long-Chain Molecules Called Polymers

1) Polymers are long molecules formed when lots of small molecules called monomers join together. This reaction is called polymerisation — and it usually needs high pressure and a catalyst.

2) Plastics are made up of polymers. They're usually carbon based and their monomers are often alkenes (see page 78).

Addition Polymers are Made From Unsaturated Monomers

1) The monomers that make up addition polymers have a double covalent bond.

2) Lots of unsaturated monomer molecules (alkenes) can open up their double bonds and join together to form polymer chains. This is called addition polymerisation.

There's another form of polymerisation you need to know about called condensation polymerisation. There's more on this on page 83.

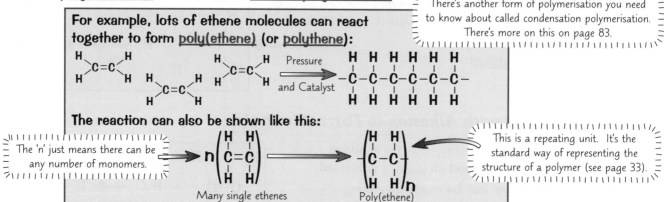

For example, lots of ethene molecules can react together to form poly(ethene) (or polythene):

The reaction can also be shown like this:

The 'n' just means there can be any number of monomers.

Many single ethenes → Poly(ethene)

This is a repeating unit. It's the standard way of representing the structure of a polymer (see page 33).

3) When the monomers react in addition polymerisation reactions, the only product is the polymer, so an addition polymer contains exactly the same type and number of atoms as the monomers that formed it.

You May Need to Draw the Repeating Unit of a Polymer

1) Drawing the displayed formula of an addition polymer from the displayed formula of its monomer is easy.

- Start by drawing the two alkene carbons, replace the double bond with a single bond and add an extra single bond to each of the carbons.
- Then fill in the rest of the groups in the same way that they surrounded the double bond in the monomer. Finally, stick a pair of brackets around the repeating bit, and put an 'n' after it (to show that there are lots of monomers).

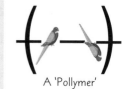

A 'Pollymer'

2) To get from the displayed formula of the polymer to the displayed formula of the monomer, just do the reverse. Draw out the repeating bit of the polymer, get rid of the two bonds going out through the brackets and put a double bond between the carbons.

Poly(chloroethene)   Chloroethene

3) The name of the polymer comes from the type of monomer it's made from — you just stick the word 'poly' in front of it and put the monomer name in brackets. So propene becomes poly(propene).

Propene   Poly(propene)

Which polymer is good for making a cuppa? Poly(putthekettleon)...

Which monomer a polymer is made from affects the properties of the plastic — as there are so many monomers, chemists can make all sorts of things. Make sure you can recognise and draw polymers and their monomers.

Q1   What is a polymer?   [1 mark]

Q2   Two different polymers can be formed from butene. This is dependent on whether the double bond of the butene monomer is located in the middle or at the end of the carbon chain.
Draw the two possible repeating units of the polymer made from butene molecules.   [2 marks]

Alcohols

Alcohol isn't just the thing your Nan has for special occasions. In fact, <u>alcohols</u> are yet another <u>homologous series</u> of organic compounds. They're handy for lots of things, and you need to know how they're used.

Alcohols Have an '-OH' Functional Group and End in '-ol'

1) The <u>general formula</u> of an alcohol is $C_nH_{2n+1}OH$. So an alcohol with 2 carbons has the formula C_2H_5OH.

2) All alcohols contain an <u>-OH group</u>. You need to know the <u>first 4</u> in the homologous series:

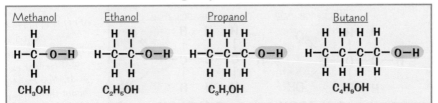

Remember — a homologous series is a group of chemicals that react in a similar way because they have the same functional group (in alcohols it's the -OH group).

3) The basic <u>naming</u> system is the same as for alkanes — but replace the final '<u>-e</u>' with '<u>-ol</u>'.

4) Don't write CH_4O instead of CH_3OH — it doesn't show the <u>-OH functional group</u>.

The First Four Alcohols Have Similar Properties

1) Alcohols are <u>flammable</u>. They undergo complete combustion in air to produce <u>carbon dioxide</u> and <u>water</u>. For example:

$$2CH_3OH_{(l)} + 3O_{2(g)} \rightarrow 2CO_{2(g)} + 4H_2O_{(g)}$$

Make sure you can write balanced equations for the combustion of alcohols.

2) Methanol, ethanol, propanol and butanol are all soluble in water. Their solutions have a <u>neutral</u> pH.

3) They also react with <u>sodium</u>. One of the products of this reaction is <u>hydrogen</u>.

4) <u>Alcohols</u> can be <u>oxidised</u> by reacting with oxygen (e.g. from the air) to produce a <u>carboxylic acid</u> (see the next page):

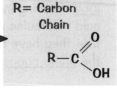

R = Carbon Chain

5) Different alcohols form different carboxylic acids. For example, <u>methanol</u> is oxidised to <u>methanoic acid</u>, while <u>ethanol</u> is oxidised to <u>ethanoic acid</u>.

Alcohols are Used as Solvents and Fuels

1) Alcohols such as methanol and ethanol are used as solvents in industry. This is because they can <u>dissolve</u> most things water can dissolve, but they can also dissolve substances that <u>water can't dissolve</u> — e.g. hydrocarbons, oils and fats.

2) The first four alcohols are used as fuels. For example, <u>ethanol</u> is used as a fuel in <u>spirit burners</u> — it burns fairly <u>cleanly</u> and it's <u>non-smelly</u>.

Ethanol can be Made by Fermentation

<u>Ethanol</u> is the alcohol found in <u>alcoholic drinks</u> such as wine or beer. It's usually made using <u>fermentation</u>.

1) <u>Fermentation</u> uses an enzyme in <u>yeast</u> to convert <u>sugars</u> into <u>ethanol</u>. Carbon dioxide is also produced. The reaction occurs in solution so the ethanol produced is aqueous.

Ethanol can also be produced from ethene. See p.79.

$$\text{sugar} \xrightarrow{\text{yeast}} \text{ethanol} + \text{carbon dioxide}$$

2) Fermentation happens fastest at a temperature of around <u>37 °C</u>, in a <u>slightly acidic</u> solution and under <u>anaerobic conditions</u> (no oxygen).

3) Under these conditions the enzyme in yeast works best to convert the sugar to alcohol. If the conditions were different, for example a <u>lower pH/higher temperature</u> or <u>higher pH/lower temperature</u>, the enzyme could be denatured (destroyed) or could work at a much slower rate.

Alcohol — drink too much and it's likely tequila...

For the exams, it might be jolly useful to learn the structures of alcohols... In fact, it might be essential...

Q1   Give the balanced equation for the complete combustion of ethanol, C_2H_5OH.   [2 marks]

Carboxylic Acids

So you would have seen a little bit about carboxylic acids on the previous page. Now it's time to dive deeper into their exciting and wondrous world... (Disclaimer: may not be exciting or wondrous.)

Carboxylic Acids Have the Functional Group -COOH

1) Carboxylic acids are a homologous series of compounds that all have '-COOH' as a functional group.

2) Their names end in '-anoic acid' (and start with the normal 'meth/eth/prop/but')

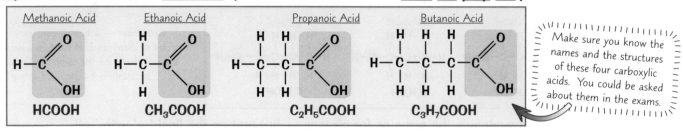

Make sure you know the names and the structures of these four carboxylic acids. You could be asked about them in the exams.

Carboxylic Acids React Like Other Acids

1) They react (like any other acid) with carbonates to produce a salt, water and carbon dioxide.

2) The salts formed in these reactions end in -anoate — e.g. methanoic acid will form a methanoate, ethanoic acid an ethanoate, etc. For example:

> ethanoic acid + sodium carbonate → sodium ethanoate + water + carbon dioxide

3) Carboxylic acids can dissolve in water. When they dissolve, they ionise and release H^+ ions resulting in an acidic solution. But, because they don't ionise completely (not all the acid molecules release their H^+ ions), they just form weak acidic solutions. This means that they have a higher pH (are less acidic) than aqueous solutions of strong acids with the same concentration. There's more about strong and weak acids on page 53.

Esters can be Made from Carboxylic Acids

1) Esters have the functional group '-COO-'.

2) Esters are formed from an alcohol and a carboxylic acid.

3) An acid catalyst is usually used (e.g. concentrated sulfuric acid).

The names of esters can be a bit complicated and are often tongue twisters. The one you need to make sure you learn is ethyl ethanoate — the examiners could ask you about this one.

> alcohol + carboxylic acid →(acid catalyst) ester + water

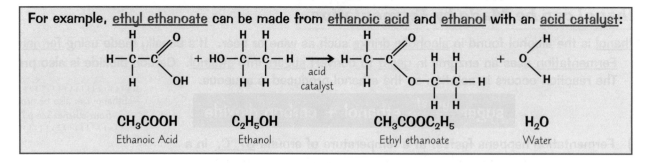

For example, ethyl ethanoate can be made from ethanoic acid and ethanol with an acid catalyst:

What's a chemist's favourite chocolate? Ester eggs...

So carboxylic acids react in the same way as normal acids, however they don't ionise fully in water which means they're weak acids. But let's not judge them on that basis, they can make esters after all.

Q1 Sodium carbonate is added to an aqueous solution of methanoic acid.
    a) Describe and explain what you would see during this reaction.   [2 marks]
    b) Give the word equation for this reaction.   [1 mark]

Condensation Polymers

You might remember <u>addition polymerisation</u> from back on page 80, but there is <u>another</u> type of polymerisation that you could be asked about. This time the monomers need to have <u>TWO</u> functional groups — gasp.

Polymers can be Made by Condensation Polymerisation

1) Condensation polymerisation involves monomers which contain <u>different</u> functional groups.

2) The monomers react together and <u>bonds</u> form between them, making polymer chains.

3) For <u>each new bond</u> that forms, a <u>small molecule</u> (for example, water) is <u>lost</u>. This is why it's called <u>condensation</u> polymerisation.

I'm a bear on a bicycle and I endorse this message.

4) The simplest types of condensation polymers contain <u>two different types</u> of monomer, each with two of the same functional groups.

5) For example, here's how a <u>polyester</u> can be made by condensation polymerisation:

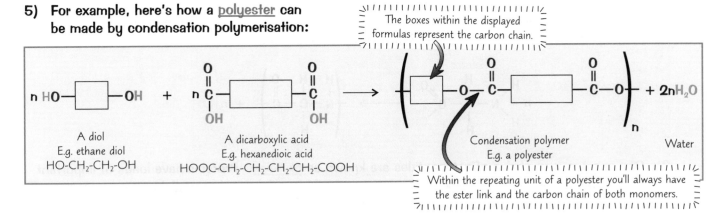

The boxes within the displayed formulas represent the carbon chain.

A diol
E.g. ethane diol
HO-CH$_2$-CH$_2$-OH

A dicarboxylic acid
E.g. hexanedioic acid
HOOC-CH$_2$-CH$_2$-CH$_2$-CH$_2$-COOH

Condensation polymer
E.g. a polyester

Water

Within the repeating unit of a polyester you'll always have the ester link and the carbon chain of both monomers.

Addition and Condensation Polymerisation are Different

Both addition and condensation polymerisation produce <u>polymers</u>. However, the <u>products</u> and <u>reactants</u> are very different:

	Addition Polymerisation	Condensation Polymerisation
<u>Number of types of monomers</u>	Only one monomer type containing a C=C bond.	Two monomer types each containing two of the same functional groups. <u>or</u> One monomer type with two different functional groups (see next page).
<u>Number of products</u>	Only one product formed.	Two types of product — the polymer and a small molecule (e.g. water).
<u>Functional groups involved in polymerisation</u>	Carbon-carbon double bond in monomer.	Two reactive groups on each monomer.

Revision's like polymers — it's all about stringing facts together...

So, addition polymers are formed when identical monomers containing C=C bonds are joined together in a polymer chain. Condensation polymers are made when different monomers, or those with two different reactive functional groups, react together. Got it? It's a bit confusing but that table should help.

Q1 Suggest what small molecule can be produced during a polymerisation reaction to form a polyester. [1 mark]

Q2 How many products are formed by an addition polymerisation reaction? [1 mark]

Naturally Occurring Polymers

Polymers might sound <u>futuristic</u> and <u>artificial</u> but they're actually found throughout the <u>natural</u> world...

Amino Acids have an Amino Group and a Carboxyl Group

1) An amino acid contains two different functional groups — a basic <u>amino group</u> (NH_2) and an acidic <u>carboxyl group</u> (COOH).

2) An example of an amino acid is <u>glycine</u> — the smallest and simplest amino acid possible.

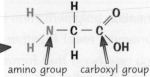

amino group   carboxyl group

Proteins are Polymers of Amino Acids

1) Amino acids can form polymers known as <u>polypeptides</u> via <u>condensation polymerisation</u>.

2) The <u>amino group</u> of an amino acid can <u>react</u> with the <u>acid group</u> of another, and so on, to form a polymer chain. For every new bond that is formed a molecule of <u>water</u> is lost.

$$n \quad \underset{\text{Glycine}}{\text{N—C—C}} \longrightarrow \left(\text{N—C—C} \right)_n + n\,H_2O$$

3) One or more <u>long-chains</u> of polypeptides are known as <u>proteins</u>. Proteins have loads of important uses in the human body. For example, enzymes work as <u>catalysts</u>, haemoglobin <u>transports oxygen</u>, <u>antibodies</u> form part of the <u>immune system</u>, and the majority of <u>body tissue</u> is made from proteins.

4) Polypeptides and proteins can contain <u>different</u> amino acids in their polymer chains. The order of the amino acids is what gives proteins their different properties and shapes.

DNA Molecules are Made From Nucleotide Polymers

<u>DNA</u> (deoxyribonucleic acid) is found in <u>every</u> living thing and many viruses. It contains <u>genetic instructions</u> that allow the organism to develop and operate. It's a large molecule that takes a <u>double helix</u> structure.

1) DNA is made of <u>two</u> polymer chains of monomers called '<u>nucleotides</u>'. The nucleotides each contain a small molecule known as a '<u>base</u>'. There are four different bases, known by their initials — A, C, G, T.

2) The bases on the different polymer chains pair up with each other and form <u>cross links</u> keeping the two strands of nucleotides <u>together</u> and giving the double helix structure.

3) The order of the bases acts as a <u>code</u> for an <u>organism's genes</u>.

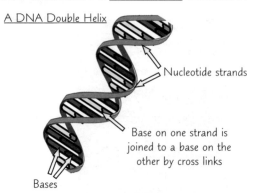

A DNA Double Helix

Nucleotide strands

Base on one strand is joined to a base on the other by cross links

Bases

Simple Sugars Can Form Polymers

1) <u>Sugars</u> are small molecules that contain <u>carbon</u>, <u>oxygen</u> and <u>hydrogen</u>.

2) Sugars can react together through polymerisation reactions to form <u>larger</u> carbohydrate <u>polymers</u>, e.g. <u>starch</u>, which living things use to store energy, and <u>cellulose</u>, which is found in <u>plant cell walls</u>.

Protein — not just for bodybuilders...

Polymers are found everywhere in nature. You can't get away from them — trust me I've tried. Even the paper on this page is made of cellulose fibres which are polymers. Like revision, there is no escape.

Q1 Amino acids can bond together by condensation polymerisation.
State the type of polymer formed from this reaction. [1 mark]

Q2 Give three examples of naturally occurring polymers. [3 marks]

Revision Questions for Topic 7

Well, that wraps up Topic 7 — I think this was my favourite topic so far, along with 1, 2, 3, 4, 5, and 6...

- Try these questions and tick off each one when you get it right.
- When you've done all the questions under a heading and are completely happy with it, tick it off.

Hydrocarbons (p.75) ☑

1) What two elements do hydrocarbons contain? ☑
2) What is the general formula for alkanes? ☑
3) Draw the displayed formula of butane. ☑
4) What two waste products form from the complete combustion of hydrocarbons? ☑

Crude Oil (p.76-77) ☑

5) How is crude oil formed? ☑
6) Where are the shortest carbon chains found in the fractional distillation column? ☑
7) Give three products that can be made from crude oil. ☑
8) Why is cracking used? ☑
9) Give a product of cracking that is used for making plastics. ☑

Alkenes and Addition Polymerisation (p.78-80) ☐

10) What is an alkene? ☑
11) Give the general formula for an alkene. ☑
12) Why do alkenes burn in air with a smoky flame? ☑
13) Name the molecule that ethene reacts with when it is hydrogenated. ☑
14) Draw the product of the reaction of ethene with bromine water. ☑
15) What is used to test for alkenes? ☑
16) What type of compounds are used as the monomers to make addition polymers? ☑
17) Draw the displayed formula for the repeat unit of poly(ethene). ☑

Alcohols and Carboxylic Acids (p.81-82) ☑

18) Give the names and formulas of the first four alcohols. ☑
19) Give the balanced equation for the combustion of methanol. ☑
20) Name the gas that is produced when ethanol reacts with sodium. ☑
21) Name the process that converts sugar to ethanol using yeast. ☑
22) Draw the displayed formula of C_2H_5COOH. ☑
23) Why are carboxylic acids considered weak acids? ☑
24) Give the general word equation for the reaction of an alcohol and a carboxylic acid. ☑

Condensation Polymerisation and Natural Polymers (p.83-84) ☑

25) How many different products are there in a condensation polymerisation reaction? ☑
26) What are polypeptides? ☑
27) What small molecule is lost when two amino acids react together to form a new bond? ☑

Purity and Formulations

In an ideal world, every compound a chemist made would be <u>100% pure</u>. Unfortunately, in the real world it <u>doesn't</u> always work out like that — but luckily, there are ways to find out <u>how pure</u> a substance is.

Purity is Defined Differently in Chemistry to Everyday

1) <u>Usually</u> when you refer to a <u>substance</u> as being <u>pure</u> you mean that <u>nothing</u> has been <u>added</u> to it, so it's in its <u>natural state</u>. For example: pure milk or beeswax.

2) In <u>chemistry</u>, a pure substance is something that only contains <u>one compound</u> or <u>element</u> throughout — not mixed with anything else.

The Boiling or Melting Point Tells You How Pure a Substance Is

1) A chemically pure substance will <u>melt</u> or <u>boil</u> at a <u>specific</u> temperature.

2) You can test the purity of a sample by measuring its <u>melting</u> or <u>boiling point</u> and comparing it with the melting or boiling point of the <u>pure substance</u> (which you can find from a <u>data book</u>).

3) The <u>closer</u> your measured value is to the actual melting or boiling point, the <u>purer</u> your sample is.

4) Impurities in your sample will <u>lower</u> the <u>melting point</u> and <u>increase</u> the <u>melting range</u> of your substance.

5) Impurities in your sample will also <u>increase</u> the <u>boiling point</u> and may result in your sample boiling at a <u>range</u> of temperatures.

Formulations are Mixtures with Exact Amounts of Components

1) <u>Formulations</u> are useful mixtures with a <u>precise purpose</u> that are made by following a 'formula' (a recipe). Each component in a formulation is present in a <u>measured quantity</u>, and <u>contributes</u> to the properties of the formulation so that it meets its <u>required function</u>.

> Take a look at p.16 for more on mixtures.

> For example, paints are formulations composed of:
> - <u>Pigment</u> — gives the paint colour, for example titanium oxide is used as a pigment in white paints.
> - <u>Solvent</u> — used to dissolve the other components and alter the viscosity.
> - <u>Binder</u> (resin) — forms a film that holds the pigment in place after it's been painted on.
> - <u>Additives</u> — added to further change the physical and chemical properties of the paint.
>
> Depending on the <u>purpose</u> of the paint, the <u>chemicals</u> used and their <u>amounts</u> will be changed so the paint produced is right for the job.

2) Formulations are really important in the <u>pharmaceutical industry</u>. For example, by altering the formulation of a pill, chemists can make sure it delivers the drug to the correct <u>part of the body</u> at the right <u>concentration</u>, that it's <u>consumable</u> and has a long enough <u>shelf life</u>.

3) In <u>everyday life</u>, formulations can be found in cleaning products, fuels, cosmetics, fertilisers (see p.105), metal alloys and even food and drink.

> I think this musical formulation needs more funk.

4) When you buy a product, you might find that it has <u>information</u> about its composition on the packaging. For example, the <u>ratio</u> or <u>percentage</u> of each component. This tells you the product's a <u>formulation</u>. It also lets you choose a formulation with the <u>right composition</u> for your particular use.

Cake and tea are key to the revision success formula...

Knowing how pure a product is can be vital in industries such as pharmaceuticals and the food industry. Luckily for us, chemists have lots of different ways to make sure they're making exactly what they want.

Q1   The melting point of a sample of aspirin made by a student is measured as being between 128-132 °C. The melting point and boiling points of pure aspirin are 136 °C and 140 °C respectively.
    a) Give two reasons why the melting point measured shows that the sample is not pure.   [2 marks]
    b) Suggest a value for the boiling point of the sample.   [1 mark]

Paper Chromatography

You met chromatography on page 16. Now it's time to see how it works. Careful — things might get crazy...

Chromatography uses Two Phases

Chromatography is an analytical method used to separate the substances in a mixture. You can then use it to identify the substances. There are different types of chromatography, but they all have two 'phases':

- A mobile phase — where the molecules can move. This is always a liquid or a gas.
- A stationary phase — where the molecules can't move. This can be a solid or a really thick liquid.

1) During a chromatography experiment, the substances in the sample constantly move between the mobile and the stationary phases — an equilibrium is formed between the two phases.

2) The mobile phase moves through the stationary phase, and anything dissolved in the mobile phase moves with it. How quickly a chemical moves depends on how it's 'distributed' between the two phases — whether it spends more time in the mobile phase or the stationary phase.

3) The chemicals that spend more time in the mobile phase than the stationary phase will move further through the stationary phase.

4) The components in a mixture will normally separate through the stationary phase, so long as all the components spend different amounts of time in the mobile phase. The number of spots may change in different solvents as the distribution of the chemical will change depending on the solvent. A pure substance will only ever form one spot in any solvent as there is only one substance in the sample.

During paper chromatography the stationary phase is the chromatography paper (often filter paper) and the mobile phase is the solvent (e.g ethanol or water). The amount of time the molecules spend in each phase depends on two things:
- How soluble they are in the solvent.
- How attracted they are to the paper.

Molecules with a higher solubility in the solvent, and which are less attracted to the paper, will spend more time in the mobile phase — and they'll be carried further up the paper.

The method for carrying out paper chromatography is on page 16.

Watch glass
Beaker
Baseline
Spots of chemicals
Sample
Solvent

You can Calculate the R_f Value for Each Chemical

PRACTICAL

1) The result of chromatography analysis is called a chromatogram.

2) An R_f value is the ratio between the distance travelled by the dissolved substance (the solute) and the distance travelled by the solvent. The further through the stationary phase a substance moves, the larger the R_f value. You can calculate R_f values using the formula:

$$R_f = \frac{\text{distance travelled by substance (B)}}{\text{distance travelled by solvent (A)}}$$

This is the distance from the baseline to the centre of the spot.

Distance moved by solvent (solvent front)
Spot of chemical
Baseline (Origin)
A
B

3) Chromatography is often carried out to see if a certain substance is present in a mixture. To do this, you run a pure sample of that substance (a reference) alongside the unknown mixture. If the R_f values of the reference and one of the spots in the mixture match, the substance may be present (although you haven't yet proved they're the same).

4) The R_f value is dependent on the solvent — if you change the solvent the R_f value for a substance will change. You can test both the mixture and the reference in a number of different solvents. If the R_f value of the reference compound matches the R_f value of one of the spots in the mixture in all the solvents, then it's likely the reference compound is present in the mixture. If the spots in the mixture and the spot in the reference only have the same R_f value in some of the solvents, then the reference compound isn't present in the mixture.

Chromatography revision — it's a phase you have to get through...

You can't see the chemicals moving between the two phases, but it does happen. You'll just have to trust me.

Q1 Explain how paper chromatography separates mixtures. [4 marks]

Tests for Gases and Anions

Ahh... tests, glorious tests. Luckily, these aren't the kind of tests you have to <u>revise</u> for, but you should probably revise these tests for your exam — it's <u>swings</u> and <u>roundabouts</u> really...

There are Tests for 4 Common Gases

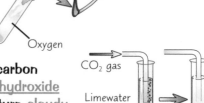

1) Chlorine

Chlorine <u>bleaches</u> damp <u>litmus paper</u>, turning it white. (It may turn <u>red</u> for a moment first though — that's because a solution of chlorine is <u>acidic</u>.)

Litmus paper

2) Oxygen

If you put a glowing splint inside a test tube containing <u>oxygen</u>, the oxygen will <u>relight</u> the <u>glowing splint</u>.

Glowing Splint

Oxygen

3) Carbon Dioxide

Bubbling carbon dioxide through (or shaking carbon dioxide with) an aqueous solution of <u>calcium hydroxide</u> (known as <u>limewater</u>) causes the solution to turn <u>cloudy</u>.

CO_2 gas

Limewater

4) Hydrogen

If you hold a <u>lit splint</u> at the open end of a test tube containing hydrogen, you'll get a "<u>squeaky pop</u>". (The noise comes from the hydrogen burning quickly with the oxygen in the air to form H_2O.)

POP!

Lighted Splint

H_2 gas

Tests for Anions Often Give Precipitates

Dilute Acid Can Help Detect Carbonates

Carbonates are substance that contain CO_3^{2-} ions. You can <u>test</u> whether a mystery solution contains carbonate ions by putting a sample in a test tube and then using a dropping pipette to add a couple of drops of <u>dilute acid</u>. You should then connect the test tube to a test tube of <u>limewater</u>. If carbonate ions are present, <u>carbon dioxide</u> will be released that will turn the limewater <u>cloudy</u> when it bubbles through it (as shown above). For example:

$$Na_2CO_{3(aq)} + 2HCl_{(aq)} \rightarrow CO_{2(g)} + 2NaCl_{(aq)} + H_2O_{(l)}$$

Test for Sulfates with HCl and Barium Chloride

To identify <u>sulfate</u> ions (SO_4^{2-}), use a dropping pipette to add a couple of drops of <u>dilute hydrochloric acid</u> (HCl) followed by a couple of drops of <u>barium chloride solution</u> ($BaCl_2$) to a test tube containing your mystery solution.

If sulfate ions are present, a white precipitate of barium sulfate will form:

$$Ba^{2+}_{(aq)} + SO_4^{2-}_{(aq)} \longrightarrow BaSO_{4(s)}$$

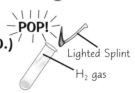

Hydrochloric acid is added to get rid of any traces of carbonate ions before you do the test. These would also produce a precipitate, so they'd confuse the results.

Test for Halides (Cl⁻, Br⁻, I⁻) with Nitric Acid and Silver Nitrate

To identify a <u>halide ion</u>, add a couple of drops of <u>dilute nitric acid</u> (HNO_3), followed by a couple of drops of <u>silver nitrate solution</u>, $AgNO_3$, to your mystery solution.

$Ag^+_{(aq)} + Cl^-_{(aq)} \longrightarrow AgCl_{(s)}$ A <u>chloride</u> gives a white precipitate of <u>silver chloride</u>.

$Ag^+_{(aq)} + Br^-_{(aq)} \longrightarrow AgBr_{(s)}$ A <u>bromide</u> gives a cream precipitate of <u>silver bromide</u>.

$Ag^+_{(aq)} + I^-_{(aq)} \longrightarrow AgI_{(s)}$ An <u>iodide</u> gives a yellow precipitate of <u>silver iodide</u>.

Hopefully this page won't be too testing for you...

How to learn this page — don't stare at the whole thing till your eyes swim and you don't want to see the word 'precipitate' ever again. Each test has been given its own section, so take them one by one and learn it that way.

Q1   A student adds dilute nitric acid and silver nitrate solution to an aqueous solution of halide ions. A white precipitate is formed. Suggest what halide may be present in the solution.   [1 mark]

Tests for Cations

I haven't met a person who doesn't like <u>flame tests</u> for positive ions — everybody loves 'em...

Flame Tests Identify Metal Ions

1) Compounds of some metals burn with a <u>characteristic colour</u>.

2) So you can test for various metal ions by heating your substance and seeing whether it <u>burns</u> with a <u>distinctive colour flame</u>:

<u>Lithium ions</u>, Li^+, burn with a crimson flame.
<u>Sodium ions</u>, Na^+, burn with a yellow flame.
<u>Potassium ions</u>, K^+, burn with a lilac flame.
<u>Calcium ions</u>, Ca^{2+}, burn with an orange-red flame.
<u>Copper ions</u>, Cu^{2+}, burn with a green flame.

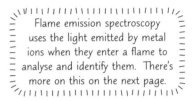

Flame emission spectroscopy uses the light emitted by metal ions when they enter a flame to analyse and identify them. There's more on this on the next page.

3) To do the test, you first need to <u>clean</u> a <u>platinum</u> wire loop by dipping it in some dilute <u>HCl</u> and then holding it in a blue flame from a Bunsen burner until it burns <u>without any colour</u>. Then, dip the loop into the <u>sample</u> you want to test and put it back in the flame. Record the <u>colour</u> of the flame.

4) You can use these <u>colours</u> to <u>detect</u> and <u>identify</u> different ions. However it only works for samples that contain a single metal ion. If the sample tested contains a <u>mixture</u> of metal ions, the flame colours of some <u>ions</u> may be <u>hidden</u> by the colours of <u>others</u>.

Some Metals Form a Coloured Precipitate with NaOH

1) Many <u>metal hydroxides</u> are <u>insoluble</u> and precipitate out of solution when formed. Some of these hydroxides have a <u>characteristic colour</u>.

2) So in this test you add a few drops of <u>sodium hydroxide</u> solution to a solution of your mystery compound — all in the hope of forming an insoluble hydroxide.

3) If you get a <u>coloured insoluble hydroxide</u> you can often tell which metal was in the compound.

Metal Ions	Colour of Precipitate	Ionic Equation for Precipitate Formation
Calcium, Ca^{2+}	White	$Ca^{2+}_{(aq)} + 2OH^-_{(aq)} \rightarrow Ca(OH)_{2\,(s)}$
Copper(II), Cu^{2+}	Blue	$Cu^{2+}_{(aq)} + 2OH^-_{(aq)} \rightarrow Cu(OH)_{2\,(s)}$
Iron(II), Fe^{2+}	Green	$Fe^{2+}_{(aq)} + 2OH^-_{(aq)} \rightarrow Fe(OH)_{2\,(s)}$
Iron(III), Fe^{3+}	Brown	$Fe^{3+}_{(aq)} + 3OH^-_{(aq)} \rightarrow Fe(OH)_{3\,(s)}$
Aluminium, Al^{3+}	White at first. But then redissolves in excess NaOH to form a colourless solution.	$Al^{3+}_{(aq)} + 3OH^-_{(aq)} \rightarrow Al(OH)_{3\,(s)}$
Magnesium, Mg^{2+}	White	$Mg^{2+}_{(aq)} + 2OH^-_{(aq)} \rightarrow Mg(OH)_{2\,(s)}$

You don't need to know the equation for how the aluminium hydroxide precipitate dissolves.

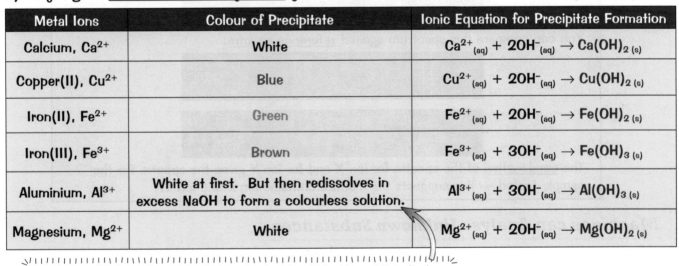

Cations — ions with a pawsitive charge...

Did you know that compounds containing metal cations are put into fireworks? And that when fireworks explode it's these metal cations that give fireworks their pretty colours? November 5th will never seem the same again...

Q1 Why can you use a flame test to identify the metal ion in a compound? [1 mark]

Q2 Sodium hydroxide is added to a solution of an unknown metal ion.
A white precipitate is formed which redissolves following the addition of excess NaOH.
a) Suggest what the unknown metal ion is. [1 mark]
b) Give the ionic equation for the formation of the precipitate. [1 mark]

Flame Emission Spectroscopy

As well as producing pretty colours, the science behind flame tests can be used to <u>identify</u> different metal ions in solution <u>accurately</u> and find their <u>concentrations</u>. Phwoar, colours and science. This is my kind of page...

Every Metal Ion Gives a Characteristic Line Spectrum

1) During <u>flame emission spectroscopy</u> a sample is placed in a flame. As the ions <u>heat up</u> their electrons become <u>excited</u>. When the electrons <u>drop</u> back to their <u>original energy levels</u>, they <u>transfer energy</u> as light.

2) The light passes through a <u>spectroscope</u>, which can detect different wavelengths of light to produce a <u>line spectrum</u>.

3) The combination of wavelengths emitted by an ion depends on its <u>charge</u> and its <u>electron arrangement</u> (see page 20). Since no two ions have the same charge <u>and</u> the same electron arrangement, <u>different ions</u> emit <u>different wavelengths</u> of light. So each ion produces a <u>different pattern</u> of wavelengths, and has a different line spectrum.

4) The <u>intensity</u> of the spectrum indicates the <u>concentration</u> of that ion in solution.

5) This means that line spectrums can be used to <u>identify ions</u> in solution and calculate their <u>concentrations</u>.

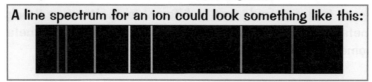

A line spectrum for an ion could look something like this:

Flame Emission Spectroscopy Works for Mixtures

Flame emission spectroscopy can also be used to identify different ions in <u>mixtures</u>. This makes it more useful than <u>flame tests</u>, which only work for substances that contain a <u>single metal ion</u>.

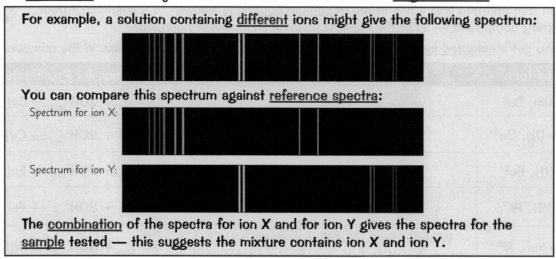

For example, a solution containing <u>different</u> ions might give the following spectrum:

You can compare this spectrum against <u>reference spectra</u>:

Spectrum for ion X:

Spectrum for ion Y:

The <u>combination</u> of the spectra for ion X and for ion Y gives the spectra for the <u>sample</u> tested — this suggests the mixture contains ion X and ion Y.

Machines can Analyse Unknown Substances

Chemists often use <u>instrumental analysis</u> (i.e tests that use machines), such as flame emission spectroscopy, <u>instead</u> of conducting tests.

Must identify ions!

<u>Advantages of Using Machines</u>:

• <u>Very sensitive</u> — they can detect even the <u>tiniest amounts</u> of substances.

• <u>Very fast</u> and tests can be automated.

• <u>Very accurate</u>.

Spectroscopy — it's a flaming useful technique...

As you can see, there are nifty ways of identifying substances as well as things like your bog standard flame test.

Q1   Why might it be necessary to use flame emission spectroscopy instead of a flame test to identify metal ions?

[2 marks]

The Evolution of the Atmosphere

Theories for how the Earth's atmosphere <u>evolved</u> have changed a lot over the years — it's hard to gather evidence from such a <u>long time period</u> and from <u>so long ago</u> (4.6 billion years). Here's one idea we've got:

Phase 1 — Volcanoes Gave Out Gases

1) The first <u>billion years</u> of Earth's history were pretty explosive — the surface was covered in <u>volcanoes</u> that erupted and released lots of gases. We think this was how the <u>early atmosphere</u> was formed.

2) The early atmosphere was probably mostly <u>carbon dioxide</u>, with <u>virtually no oxygen</u>. This is quite like the atmospheres of <u>Mars</u> and <u>Venus</u> today.

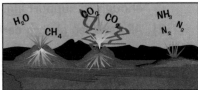

3) Volcanic activity also released <u>nitrogen</u>, which built up in the atmosphere over time, as well as <u>water vapour</u> and small amounts of <u>methane</u> and <u>ammonia</u>.

Phase 2 — Oceans, Algae and Green Plants Absorbed Carbon Dioxide

1) When the water vapour in the atmosphere <u>condensed</u>, it formed the <u>oceans</u>.

2) Lots of carbon dioxide was removed from the early atmosphere as it <u>dissolved</u> in the oceans. This dissolved carbon dioxide then went through a series of reactions to form <u>carbonate precipitates</u> that formed <u>sediments</u> on the <u>seabed</u>.

3) <u>Green plants</u> and <u>algae</u> evolved and absorbed some of the carbon dioxide so that they could carry out <u>photosynthesis</u> (see below). Later, marine <u>animals</u> evolved. Their <u>shells</u> and <u>skeletons</u> contained <u>carbonates</u> from the oceans.

4) Some of the carbon these organisms took in from the atmosphere and oceans became locked up in <u>rocks</u> and <u>fossil fuels</u> after the organisms died.

   • When plants, plankton and marine animals <u>die</u>, they fall to the seabed and get <u>buried</u> by <u>layers of sediment</u>. Over millions of years, they become <u>compressed</u> and form <u>sedimentary rocks</u>, <u>oil</u> and <u>gas</u> — trapping the carbon within them and helping to keep carbon dioxide levels in the atmosphere <u>reduced</u>.

   • Things like coal, crude oil and natural gas that are made by this process are called '<u>fossil fuels</u>'.

   • <u>Crude oil</u> and <u>natural gas</u> are formed from deposits of <u>plankton</u>. These fossil fuels form reservoirs under the seabed when they get <u>trapped</u> in rocks.

   • <u>Coal</u> is a sedimentary rock made from thick <u>plant deposits</u>.

   • <u>Limestone</u> is also a sedimentary rock. It's mostly made of <u>calcium carbonate</u> deposits from the <u>shells</u> and <u>skeletons</u> of marine organisms.

Phase 3 — Green Plants and Algae Produced Oxygen

1) As well as absorbing the carbon dioxide in the atmosphere, green plants and algae produced oxygen by <u>photosynthesis</u> — this is when plants use light to convert carbon dioxide and water into <u>sugars</u>:

2) Algae evolved <u>first</u> — about <u>2.7 billion</u> years ago. Then over the next <u>billion years</u> or so, green plants also evolved.

$$carbon\ dioxide + water \xrightarrow{light} glucose + oxygen$$
$$6CO_2 + 6H_2O \xrightarrow{light} C_6H_{12}O_6 + 6O_2$$

3) As oxygen levels built up in the atmosphere over time, more <u>complex life</u> (like animals) could evolve.

4) Eventually, about <u>200 million years ago</u>, the atmosphere reached a composition similar to what it is <u>today</u>: approximately 80% nitrogen, 20% oxygen and small amounts of other gases (each only makes up less than 1% of the atmosphere), mainly carbon dioxide, noble gases and water vapour.

The atmosphere's evolving — shut the window will you...

We've learnt about the atmosphere from Antarctic ice cores. Each year, a layer of ice forms with bubbles of air trapped in it. The deeper the ice, the older the air, so examining air in different layers shows us how it's changed.

Q1   Describe how sedimentary rocks are formed.   [2 marks]

Greenhouse Gases and Climate Change

Greenhouse gases are important but can also cause problems — it's all about keeping a delicate balance.

Carbon Dioxide is a Greenhouse Gas

Short wavelength radiation
Long wavelength radiation
Greenhouse gases

1) Greenhouse gases like carbon dioxide, methane and water vapour act like an insulating layer in the Earth's atmosphere — this, amongst other factors, allows the Earth to be warm enough to support life.

2) All particles absorb certain frequencies of radiation. Greenhouse gases don't absorb the incoming short wavelength radiation from the sun — but they do absorb the long wavelength radiation that gets reflected back off the Earth. Then they re-radiate it in all directions — including back towards the Earth. The longwave radiation is thermal radiation, so it results in warming of the surface of the Earth. This is the greenhouse effect.

3) Some forms of human activity affect the amount of greenhouse gases in the atmosphere. E.g:

- Deforestation: fewer trees means less CO_2 is removed from the atmosphere via photosynthesis.
- Burning fossil fuels: carbon that was 'locked up' in these fuels is released as CO_2.
- Agriculture: more farm animals produce more methane through their digestive processes.
- Creating waste: more landfill sites and more waste from agriculture means more CO_2 and methane released by decomposition of waste.

Increasing Carbon Dioxide is Linked to Climate Change

1) The Earth's temperature varies naturally, but recently the average temperature of the Earth's surface has been increasing. Most scientists agree that the extra carbon dioxide from human activity is causing this increase and that this will lead to climate change.

2) Evidence for this has been peer-reviewed (see page 2) — so you know that the information out there is reliable.

3) Unfortunately, it's hard to fully understand the Earth's climate — this is because it's so complex, and there are so many variables, that it's very hard to make a model that isn't oversimplified.

4) This has led to speculation, particularly in the media — where stories may be biased or only some of the information given.

See page 3 for more on science in the media.

Climate Change Could Have Dangerous Consequences

The Earth's climate is complex, but it's still important to make predictions about the consequences of climate change so that policy-makers can make decisions now. For example:

1) An increase in global temperature could lead to polar ice caps melting — causing a rise in sea levels, increased flooding in coastal areas and coastal erosion.

2) Changes in rainfall patterns (the amount, timing and distribution) may cause some regions to get too much or too little water. This, along with changes in temperature, may affect the ability of certain regions to produce food.

3) The frequency and severity of storms may also increase.

4) Changes in temperature and the amount of water available in a habitat may affect wild species, leading to differences in their distribution.

Eee, problems, problems — there's always summat goin' wrong...

Everyone's talking about climate change these days — it's pretty scary stuff, so make sure you get it.

Q1   Describe three potential consequences of climate change.   [3 marks]

Carbon Footprints

It's generally accepted that greenhouse gas emissions from <u>human activities</u> is causing <u>climate change</u>. Knowing what leads to <u>a lot</u> of emissions of carbon dioxide could be useful for <u>stopping</u> it happening.

Carbon Footprints are Tricky to Measure

1) Carbon footprints are basically a <u>measure</u> of the amount of <u>carbon dioxide</u> and other <u>greenhouse gases</u> released over the <u>full life cycle</u> of something. That can be a service (e.g. the school bus), an event (e.g. the Olympics), a product (e.g. a toastie maker) — almost <u>anything</u>.

2) <u>Measuring</u> the total carbon footprint of something can be <u>really hard</u>, though — or even <u>impossible</u>.

3) That's because there are so many <u>different factors</u> to consider — for example, you would have to count the emissions released as a result of <u>sourcing all the parts</u> of your toastie maker and in <u>making it</u>, not to mention the emissions produced when you <u>actually use it</u> and finally <u>dispose</u> of it. Eugh, complicated...

4) Still, a <u>rough calculation</u> can give a good idea of what the <u>worst emitters</u> are — so that people can <u>avoid them</u> in the future.

There are Ways of Reducing Carbon Footprints

You can't always measure a carbon footprint <u>exactly</u>, but there are always methods to try and <u>reduce it</u>. Anything that <u>reduces</u> the amount of <u>greenhouse gases</u> (e.g. carbon dioxide or methane) given out by a process will also reduce its carbon footprint. Here are some things that can be done:

- <u>Renewable energy sources</u> or <u>nuclear energy</u> could be used instead of <u>fossil fuels</u>.
- Using more <u>efficient processes</u> could <u>conserve energy</u> and cut <u>waste</u>. Lots of waste <u>decomposes</u> to release <u>methane</u>, so this will reduce methane emissions.
- Governments could <u>tax</u> companies or individuals based on the amount of greenhouse gases they <u>emit</u> — e.g. taxing <u>cars</u> based on the amount of <u>carbon dioxide</u> they emit over a set distance could mean that people <u>choose</u> to buy ones that are more <u>fuel-efficient</u> and so less polluting.
- Governments can also put a <u>cap</u> on emissions of <u>all</u> greenhouse gases that companies make — then <u>sell licences</u> for emissions <u>up to</u> that cap.
- There's also technology that <u>captures</u> the CO_2 produced by burning fossil fuels <u>before</u> it's released into the atmosphere — it can then be <u>stored deep underground</u> in cracks in the rock such as old <u>oil wells</u>.

But Making Reductions is Still Difficult

1) It's easy enough <u>saying</u> that we should cut emissions, but <u>actually doing it</u> — that's a <u>different story</u>.

2) For a start, there's still a lot of work to be done on <u>alternative technologies</u> that result in <u>lower</u> CO_2 emissions.

3) A lot of <u>governments</u> are also worried that making these changes will impact on the <u>economic growth</u> of communities — which could be <u>bad</u> for people's <u>well-being</u>. This is particularly important for countries that are <u>still developing</u>.

4) Because not everyone is on board, it's hard to make <u>international agreements</u> to reduce emissions. Most countries don't want to <u>sacrifice</u> their <u>economic development</u> if they think that others <u>won't do the same</u>.

5) It's not just governments, though — <u>individuals</u> in developed countries need to make changes to their <u>lifestyles</u>. But it might be <u>hard</u> to get people to make changes if they <u>don't want to</u> and if there isn't <u>enough education</u> provided about <u>why</u> the changes are necessary and <u>how</u> to make them.

Who has the biggest carbon footprint then? Clowns of course...

Carbon footprints are a game of 'fortunately/unfortunately'. Unfortunately, carbon emissions can lead to global warming. Fortunately, there are steps we can take to cut our carbon dioxide emissions. Unfortunately, not everyone's on board. Fortunately, as time goes on, people are doing more to reduce their emissions. And so on...

Q1 State two things governments can do to try to reduce the greenhouse gas emissions of businesses. [2 marks]

Air Pollution

Increasing carbon dioxide is causing climate change. But CO_2 isn't the only gas released when fossil fuels burn — you also get other nasties like oxides of nitrogen, sulfur dioxide and carbon monoxide.

Combustion of Fossil Fuels Releases Gases and Particles

1) Fossil fuels, such as crude oil and coal, contain hydrocarbons. During combustion, the carbon and hydrogen in these compounds are oxidised so that carbon dioxide and water vapour are released into the atmosphere.

Hydrocarbons are compounds that only contain hydrogen and carbon (see page 75).

2) When there's plenty of oxygen, all the fuel burns — this is called complete combustion.

3) If there's not enough oxygen, some of the fuel doesn't burn — this is called incomplete combustion. Under these conditions, solid particles (called particulates) of soot (carbon) and unburnt fuel are released and carbon monoxide can be produced as well as carbon dioxide.

4) Particulates in the air can cause all sorts of problems:

There's more about complete combustion on p.75 and incomplete combustion on p.78.

- If particulates are inhaled, they can get stuck in the lungs and cause damage. This can then lead to respiratory problems.

- They're also bad for the environment — they themselves, or the clouds they help to produce, reflect sunlight back into space. This means that less light reaches the Earth — causing global dimming.

5) It's not just particulates from incomplete combustion that cause problems. Carbon monoxide is pretty nasty too.

- Carbon monoxide (CO) is really dangerous because it can stop your blood from doing its proper job of carrying oxygen around the body.
- It does this by binding to the haemoglobin in your blood that normally carries O_2 — so less oxygen is able to be transported round your body.
- A lack of oxygen in the blood can lead to fainting, a coma or even death.
- Carbon monoxide doesn't have any colour or smell, so it's very hard to detect. This makes it even more dangerous.

Sulfur Dioxide and Oxides of Nitrogen Can be Released

1) Sulfur dioxide (SO_2) is released during the combustion of fossil fuels, such as coal, that contain sulfur impurities — the sulfur in the fuel becomes oxidised.

2) Nitrogen oxides are created from a reaction between the nitrogen and oxygen in the air, caused by the heat of the burning. (This can happen in the internal combustion engines of cars.)

SO_2 gas reacts with water to form sulfuric acid. You can test for sulfur impurities in a fuel by bubbling the gases from combustion through a solution containing Universal indicator — if the fuel contains sulfur, the gases will contain SO_2 which will form sulfuric acid and turn the Universal indicator red.

3) When these gases mix with clouds they form dilute sulfuric acid or dilute nitric acid. This then falls as acid rain.

4) Acid rain kills plants and damages buildings and statues. It also makes metal corrode. It's shocking.

5) Not only that, but sulfur dioxide and nitrogen oxides can also be bad for human health — they cause respiratory problems if they're breathed in.

Revision and pollution — the two bugbears of modern life...

Eeee.... cars and fossil fuels — they're nowt but trouble. But at least this topic is kind of interesting, what with its relevance to everyday life and all. Just think... you could see this kind of stuff on TV.

Q1 Name three potential pollutants that could be released as a result of incomplete combustion of hydrocarbons, that wouldn't be released as a result of complete combustion. [3 marks]

Revision Questions for Topics 8 & 9

That's all for Topics 8 and 9, but before you breathe a sigh of relief, there are some questions to get through.

- Try these questions and tick off each one when you get it right.
- When you've done all the questions under a heading and are completely happy with it, tick it off.

Purity, Formulations and Paper Chromatography (p.86-87)

1) What is a formulation?

2) What are the two phases called in chromatography?

3) In paper chromatography, how many spots will a pure substance form on the paper?

4) Give the formula for working out the R_f value of a substance.

5) Would you expect the R_f value of a substance to change if you changed the solvent used in the chromatography experiment?

Chemical Tests (p.88-89)

6) What colour does litmus paper turn in the presence of chlorine?

7) Describe a test you could use to test for the presence of carbonate ions.

8) How do you conduct a flame test?

9) What colour precipitate do iron(II) compounds form with sodium hydroxide?

10) What occurs on addition of excess sodium hydroxide to a solution containing Al^{3+} ions?

11) Give the ionic equation for the formation of a precipitate when a solution containing magnesium ions is reacted with sodium hydroxide.

Flame Emission Spectroscopy (p.90)

12) Describe how flame emission spectroscopy works.

13) What does the intensity of a flame emission spectrum of a solution relate to?

14) Give three advantages of using machines to conduct chemical analysis.

The Evolution of the Atmosphere (p.91)

15) How do scientists think the atmosphere was formed during the first billion years or so of Earth's history?

16) Name five gases that scientists think were present in the early atmosphere.

17) Describe how the levels of carbon dioxide in the atmosphere were reduced.

18) Write the balanced chemical equation for photosynthesis.

19) State the approximate composition of the atmosphere today.

Pollution and Climate Change (p.92-94)

20) Name three greenhouse gases.

21) Explain how the greenhouse effect works to keep the Earth warm.

22) State three ways in which human activity is leading to an increase in carbon dioxide in the atmosphere.

23) What is a carbon footprint?

24) Explain why reducing carbon dioxide emissions can be a difficult issue.

25) Describe how the following air pollutants are produced:
   a) particulates,   b) carbon monoxide,   c) sulfur dioxide,   d) nitrogen oxides.

26) Why is carbon monoxide dangerous?

27) Explain how acid rain forms.

28) State two problems caused by acid rain.

Topic 9 — Chemistry of the Atmosphere

Ceramics, Composites and Polymers

We've got very good at using <u>materials</u> from the earth to produce things we can use to make our lives <u>easier</u>.

Ceramics Come in Many Different Forms

<u>Ceramics</u> are <u>non-metal</u> solids with high <u>melting points</u> that aren't made from carbon-based compounds.

1) Some ceramics can be made from <u>clay</u>.
2) <u>Clay</u> is a <u>soft</u> material when it's dug up out of the ground, so can be <u>moulded</u> into different <u>shapes</u>.
3) When it's <u>fired</u> at high temperatures, it <u>hardens</u> to form a clay ceramic.
4) Its ability to be moulded when wet and then hardened makes clay <u>ideal</u> for making <u>pottery</u> and <u>bricks</u>.
5) Another example of a ceramic is <u>glass</u>. Glass is generally <u>transparent</u>, can be <u>moulded</u> when hot and can be <u>brittle</u> when thin.
6) Most glass made is <u>soda-lime glass</u>, which is made by heating a mixture of <u>limestone</u>, <u>sand</u> and <u>sodium carbonate</u> (soda) until it melts. When the mixture cools it comes out as <u>glass</u>.
7) <u>Borosilicate glass</u> has a higher <u>melting point</u> than soda-lime glass. It's made in the same way as soda-lime glass, using a mixture of <u>sand</u> and <u>boron trioxide</u>.

Composites are Generally Made of Two Different Materials

<u>Composites</u> are made of one material <u>embedded</u> in another. <u>Fibres</u> or <u>fragments</u> of a material (known as the <u>reinforcement</u>) are surrounded by a <u>matrix</u> acting as a <u>binder</u>. The <u>properties</u> of a composite depend on the properties of the materials it is <u>made from</u>. For example:

1) <u>Fibreglass</u> consists of fibres of <u>glass</u> embedded in a matrix made of <u>polymer</u> (plastic). It has a <u>low density</u> (like plastic) but is <u>very strong</u> (like glass). It's used for things like skis, boats and surfboards.
2) <u>Carbon fibre</u> composites also have a polymer matrix. The reinforcement is either made from long chains of carbon atoms bonded together (carbon fibres) or from carbon nanotubes (see p.34). These composites are very <u>strong</u> and <u>light</u> so are used in aerospace and sports car manufacturing.
3) <u>Concrete</u> is made from <u>aggregate</u> (a mixture of sand and gravel) embedded in <u>cement</u>. It's very <u>strong</u>. This makes it ideal for use as a <u>building material</u>, e.g. in skate parks.
4) <u>Wood</u> is a natural composite of <u>cellulose fibres</u> held together by an organic polymer matrix.

Polymers Can Have Very Different Properties

Two important things can <u>influence</u> the <u>properties</u> of a polymer — <u>how</u> it's made and <u>what</u> it's made from.

For example, the properties of poly(ethene) depend on the <u>catalyst</u> that was used and the <u>reaction conditions</u> (the temperature and pressure) that it was made under.

- <u>Low density</u> (LD) poly(ethene) is made from ethene at a <u>moderate temperature</u> under a <u>high pressure</u> and with a catalyst. It's <u>flexible</u> and is used for bags and bottles.
- <u>High density</u> (HD) poly(ethene) is also made from ethene but at a <u>lower</u> temperature and pressure with a different catalyst. It's <u>more rigid</u> and is used for water tanks and drainpipes.

The <u>monomers</u> that a polymer is made from determine the type of bonds that form between the polymer chains. These weak bonds <u>between</u> the different molecule chains determine the <u>properties</u> of the polymer:

- <u>Thermosoftening polymers</u> contain individual polymer chains entwined together with weak forces between the chains. You can melt these plastics and remould them.
- <u>Thermosetting polymers</u> contain <u>monomers</u> that can form <u>cross-links</u> between the polymer chains, holding the chains together in a <u>solid structure</u>. Unlike thermosoftening polymers, these polymers <u>don't soften</u> when they're <u>heated</u>. Thermosetting polymers are strong, hard and rigid.

People in soda-lime glass houses shouldn't throw heated objects...

Modern day composites are amazing. I reckon one will end up running the country — David Carbonron.

Q1   Give one difference in properties between thermosetting and thermosoftening polymers.   [1 mark]

Properties of Materials

It's all very well making something, but the material it's made from needs to be <u>fit for purpose</u>.

Different Materials are Suited to Different Jobs

What materials are used for depends on their <u>properties</u>. You need to be able to <u>interpret information</u> about the properties of materials and decide <u>how suitable</u> these materials would be for different purposes.

<u>Ceramics</u> include <u>glass</u> and <u>clay ceramics</u> such as <u>porcelain</u> and <u>bricks</u>. They're <u>insulators</u> of heat and electricity, <u>brittle</u> (they aren't very flexible and break easily) and <u>stiff</u>.

<u>Polymers</u> are <u>insulators</u> of heat and electricity, they can be <u>flexible</u> (they can be bent without breaking) and are <u>easily moulded</u>. Polymers have many applications including in clothing and insulators in electrical items.

The properties of <u>composites</u> depend on the <u>matrix/binder</u> and the <u>reinforcement</u> used to make them, so they have many different uses.

<u>Metals</u> are <u>malleable</u>, <u>good conductors</u> of <u>heat</u> and electricity, <u>ductile</u> (they can be drawn into <u>wires</u>), <u>shiny</u> and <u>stiff</u> (see p.23). Metals have many uses, including in electrical wires, car body-work, and cutlery.

EXAMPLE: Suggest which material would be best for making the hull of a large ship.

Material	Brittleness	Water resistance
Clay ceramic	brittle	porous (absorbs water)
Rigid PVC (a polymer)	brittle	non-porous, corrosion resistant
Low carbon steel	tough	non-porous, corrodes in water, but cheap to protect against corrosion.

Low carbon steel is non-porous, strong and can be easily protected against corrosion.

1) A ship's hull needs to be <u>non-porous</u> so it doesn't absorb water, and shouldn't <u>corrode</u>. This rules out clay ceramic — it absorbs water so the ship could sink. Low carbon steel corrodes when unprotected, but it's cheap to protect so could still be suitable.

2) If the hull's <u>brittle</u>, it could suddenly break. Rigid PVC is brittle, so not suitable.

Low carbon steel looks like the best choice.

Pure Metals Don't Always Have the Properties Needed

An unsuitable material.

1) As you saw on page 35, the regular structure of pure metals makes them <u>soft</u> — often too soft for use in everyday life.

2) <u>Alloys</u> are made by adding another element to the metal. This disrupts the structure of the metal, making alloys <u>harder</u> than pure metals.

3) For example, alloys of iron called <u>steels</u> are often used instead of pure iron. Steels are made by adding <u>small</u> amounts of <u>carbon</u> and sometimes <u>other metals</u> to iron.

4) Many other <u>alloys</u> are used in everyday life.

TYPE OF STEEL	PROPERTIES	USE
Low carbon steel (0.1–0.3% carbon)	easily shaped	car bodies
High carbon steel (0.22–2.5% carbon)	very strong, inflexible, brittle	bridges
Stainless steel (chromium added, and sometimes nickel)	corrosion-resistant, hard	cutlery

For more on the structure of metals have a look at p.35.

- <u>Bronze = Copper + Tin</u>: Bronze is harder than copper. It's used to make medals, decorative ornaments and statues.

- <u>Brass = Copper + Zinc</u>: Brass is more malleable than bronze and is used in situations where lower friction is required, such as in water taps and door fittings.

- <u>Gold alloys are used to make jewellery</u>: Pure gold is very soft. Metals such as zinc, copper, and silver are used to harden the gold. Pure gold is described as 24 carat, so 18 carats means that 18 out of 24 parts of the alloy are pure gold. In other words, 18 carat gold is 75% gold.

- <u>Aluminium alloys are used to make aircraft</u>: Aluminium has a low density which is an important property in aircraft manufacture. But pure aluminium is too soft for making aeroplanes so it's alloyed with small amounts of other metals to make it stronger.

A brass band — harder than Iron Maiden...

There's a perfect purpose for every material out there — makes me believe in love again.

Q1 To the nearest percent, what percentage of pure gold is in 14 carat gold? [1 mark]

Corrosion

Some metals <u>react</u> with substances in their environment, and this can <u>weaken</u> them.

Iron and Steel Corrode Much More than Aluminium

Corrosion is where metals react with substances in their environment and are gradually destroyed.

1) Iron corrodes easily. In other words, it <u>rusts</u>. ◄——— The word "rust" is only used for the corrosion of iron, not other metals.

2) In order to rust, iron needs to be in contact with both <u>oxygen</u> and <u>water</u>, which are present in air.

3) The stuff we call rust is actually the compound hydrated iron(III) oxide. Here's the equation for it's formation:

 Iron is oxidised.

> iron + oxygen + water → hydrated iron(III) oxide

4) Corrosion only happens on the surface of a material, where it's exposed to the air.

5) Unfortunately, rust is a soft crumbly solid that soon <u>flakes off</u> to leave more iron available to <u>rust</u> again. This means that, eventually, all the iron in an object corrodes away even if it wasn't initially at the surface.

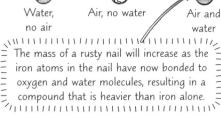

Iron(III) oxide flakes

Iron exposed to the surface as rust flakes away.

Iron

6) <u>Aluminium</u> also corrodes when exposed to air. Unlike iron objects, things made from aluminium <u>aren't</u> completely destroyed by corrosion. This is because the <u>aluminium oxide</u> that forms when aluminium corrodes <u>doesn't flake away</u>. In fact, it forms a nice <u>protective layer</u> that sticks firmly to the aluminium below and <u>stops</u> any <u>further reaction</u> taking place.

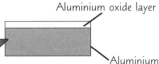

Aluminium oxide layer

Aluminium

Both Air and Water are Needed for Iron to Rust

Experiments can show that both oxygen and water are needed for iron to rust.

1) If you put an <u>iron nail</u> in a boiling tube with just <u>water</u>, it <u>won't rust</u>. (The water is boiled to remove oxygen and oil is used to stop air getting in.)

2) If you put an <u>iron nail</u> in a boiling tube with just <u>air</u>, it <u>won't rust</u>. (Calcium chloride can be used to absorb any water from the air.)

3) However, if you put an <u>iron nail</u> in a boiling tube with <u>air</u> and <u>water</u>, it <u>will rust</u>.

Oil

Boiled water

Calcium chloride

Water, no air

Air, no water

Air and water

The mass of a rusty nail will increase as the iron atoms in the nail have now bonded to oxygen and water molecules, resulting in a compound that is heavier than iron alone.

There are Two Main Ways to Prevent Rusting

1) The obvious way to prevent rusting is to <u>coat the iron</u> with a <u>barrier</u> to keep out the water and oxygen. This can be done by:

- <u>Painting/Coating with plastic</u> — ideal for big and small structures alike. It can be decorative too.
- <u>Electroplating</u> — this uses electrolysis to reduce metal ions onto an iron electrode. It can be used to coat the iron with a layer of a different metal that won't be corroded away.
- <u>Oiling/Greasing</u> — this has to be used when moving parts are involved, like on bike chains.

2) Another method is the <u>sacrificial method</u>. This involves placing a <u>more reactive metal</u> such as <u>zinc</u> or <u>magnesium</u> with the iron. Water and oxygen then react with the sacrificial metal <u>instead</u> of with the iron.

3) Some protection techniques employ both the methods above. For example:

> An object can be <u>galvanised</u> by spraying it with a <u>coating of zinc</u>. The zinc layer is firstly <u>protective</u>, but if it's <u>scratched</u>, the zinc around the site of the scratch works as a <u>sacrificial metal</u>.

The sacrificial method — chemistry sure is bloodthirsty...

If you've wondered how Iron Man avoids rusting, he greases himself up and sends out Zinc Man if it's raining.

Q1   Two nails are left in a test tube containing water and air for a period of time. One nail is galvanised, the other is pure iron. Predict which nail will rust and give a reason for your answer.   [2 marks]

Finite and Renewable Resources

There are lots of different resources that humans use to provide energy for things like heating or travelling, as well as for building materials and food. Some of these resources get replaced, some don't.

Natural Resources Come From the Earth, Sea and Air

1) Natural resources form without human input. They include anything that comes from the earth, sea or air. For example, cotton for clothing or oil for fuel.

2) Some of these natural products can be replaced by synthetic products or improved upon by man-made processes. For example, rubber is a natural product that can be extracted from the sap of a tree, however man-made polymers have now been made which can replace rubber in uses such as tyres.

3) Agriculture provides conditions where natural resources can be enhanced for our needs. E.g. the development of fertilisers have meant we can produce a high yield of crops.

Some Natural Resources will Run Out

1) Renewable resources reform at a similar rate to, or faster than, we use them.

2) For example, timber is a renewable resource as trees can be planted following a harvest and only take a few years to regrow. Other examples of renewable resources include fresh water and food.

3) Finite (non-renewable) resources, aren't formed quickly enough to be considered replaceable.

4) Finite resources include fossil fuels and nuclear fuels such as uranium and plutonium. Minerals and metals found in ores in the earth are also non-renewable materials.

5) After they've been extracted, many finite resources undergo man-made processes to provide fuels and materials necessary for modern life. For example, fractional distillation (see p.76) is used to produce usable products such as petrol from crude oil and metal ores are reduced to produce a pure metal (see p.56).

Tables, Charts and Graphs can Give You an Insight Into Different Resources

You may be asked to interpret information about resources in the exam.

 **EXAMPLE:** The table below shows information for two resources, coal and timber. Identify which resource is which.

	Energy Density (MJ/m^3)	Time it takes to form
Resource 1	7 600-11 400	10 years
Resource 2	23 000-26 000	10^6 years

The time it takes for Resource 1 to reform is 10^5 times shorter than Resource 2 suggesting it is a renewable resource. Resource 1 is also a far less energetic fuel than Resource 2, so is more likely to be timber than coal.

Resource 1 is timber and Resource 2 is coal.

10^6 is a shorthand way of showing 1 000 000. This is because $10^6 = 10 \times 10 \times 10 \times 10 \times 10 \times 10 = 1 000 000$.

Extracting Finite Resources has Risks

1) Many modern materials are made from raw, finite resources, for example most plastics, metals and building materials.

2) People have to balance the social, economic and environmental effects of extracting finite resources.

3) For example, mining metal ores is good because useful products can be made. It also provides local people with jobs and brings money into the area. However, mining ores is bad for the environment as it uses loads of energy, scars the landscape, produces lots of waste and destroys habitats.

This book is a renewable resource — a gift that keeps on giving...

Unfortunately we can't just run around using every resource we get our hands on — we have to consider the impacts of our actions. If you ever start a major mining project think... What would David Attenborough do?

Q1 Using examples, state the difference between a finite and renewable resource. [2 marks]

Reuse and Recycling

Many materials used in the modern world are limited. Once they're finished with, it's usually
far better to recycle them than to use new finite resources which will eventually run out.

Chemistry is Improving Sustainability

1) Sustainable development is an approach to development that takes account of the
needs of present society while not damaging the lives of future generations.

2) As you saw on the last page, not all resources are renewable so it's unsustainable to keep using them.

3) As well as using resources, extracting resources can be unsustainable due to the amount of energy
used and waste produced. Processing the resources into useful materials, such as glass or bricks,
can be unsustainable too, as the processes often use energy that's made from finite resources.

4) One way of reducing the use of finite resources is for people to use less.
This doesn't just reduce the use of that resource but also anything needed to produce it.

5) We can't stop using finite resources altogether, but chemists can develop and adapt processes that
use lower amounts of finite resources and reduce damage to the environment. For example, chemists
have developed catalysts that reduce the amount of energy required for certain industrial processes.

Copper-Rich Ores are in Short Supply

1) Copper is a finite resource. One way to improve its sustainability is by extracting it from low-grade
ores (ores without much copper in). Scientists are looking into new ways of doing this:

- Bioleaching — bacteria are used to convert copper compounds in the ore into soluble copper
compounds, separating out the copper from the ore in the process. The leachate (the solution
produced by the process) contains copper ions, which can be extracted, e.g. by electrolysis
(see p.58) or displacement (see p.57) with a more reactive metal, e.g. scrap iron.

- Phytomining — this involves growing plants in soil that contains copper. The plants can't use or get rid of the copper so
it gradually builds up in the leaves. The plants can be harvested, dried and burned in a furnace. The ash contains soluble
copper compounds from which copper can be extracted by electrolysis or displacement using scrap iron.

These methods can be used to extract other metals too.

2) Traditional methods of copper mining are pretty damaging to the environment. These new
methods of extraction have a much smaller impact, but the disadvantage is that they're slow.

Recycling Metals is Important

Recycling is way to reduce our need for copper rich ores.

1) Mining and extracting metals takes lots of energy, most of which comes from burning fossil fuels.

2) Recycling metals often uses much less energy than is needed to mine and extract new metal, conserves
the finite amount of each metal in the earth and cuts down on the amount of waste getting sent to landfill.

3) Metals are usually recycled by melting them and then casting them into the shape of the new product.

4) Depending on what the metal will be used for after recycling, the amount of separation required for
recyclable metals can change. For example, waste steel and
iron can be kept together as they can both be added to iron
in a blast furnace to reduce the amount of iron ore required.

A blast furnace is used to extract iron from its ore at a high temperature using carbon.

Glass can Also be Recycled

Glass recycling can help sustainability by reducing the amount of energy needed to make new glass
products, and also the amount of waste created when used glass is thrown away.

1) Glass bottles can often be reused without reshaping.

2) Other forms of glass can't be reused so they're recycled instead. Usually the glass
is separated by colour and chemical composition before being recycled.

3) The glass is crushed and then melted to be reshaped for use in glass products such as bottles or jars.
It might also be used for a different purpose such as insulating glass wool for wall insulation in homes.

CGP Jokes — 85% recycled since 1996...

Recycling is really handy — as well as saving limited finite materials it also saves energy.

Q1   Give three positive effects of recycling metals.   [3 marks]

Life Cycle Assessments

If a company wants to manufacture a new product, they carry out a life cycle assessment (LCA).

Life Cycle Assessments Show Total Environmental Costs

A life cycle assessment (LCA) looks at every stage of a product's life to assess the impact it would have on the environment.

1 Getting the Raw Materials:

1) Extracting raw materials needed for a product can damage the local environment, e.g. mining metals. Extraction can also result in pollution due to the amount of energy needed.
2) Raw materials often need to be processed to extract the desired materials and this often needs large amounts of energy. E.g. extracting metals from ores or fractional distillation of crude oil.

2 Manufacture and Packaging:

1) Manufacturing products and their packaging can use a lot of energy resources and can also cause a lot of pollution, e.g. harmful fumes such as carbon monoxide or hydrogen chloride.
2) You also need to think about any waste products and how to dispose of them. The chemical reactions used to make compounds from their raw materials can produce waste products. Some waste can be turned into other useful chemicals, reducing the amount that ends up polluting the environment.

3 Using the Product:

1) The use of a product can damage the environment. For example, burning fuels releases greenhouse gases and other harmful substances. Fertilisers can leach into streams and rivers causing damage to ecosystems.
2) How long a product is used for or how many uses it gets is also a factor — products that need lots of energy to produce but are used for ages mean less waste in the long run.

4 Product Disposal:

1) Products are often disposed of in landfill sites. This takes up space and pollutes land and water, e.g. if paint washes off a product and gets into rivers.
2) Energy is used to transport waste to landfill, which causes pollutants to be released into the atmosphere.
3) Products might be incinerated (burnt), which causes air pollution.

You Can Compare Life Cycle Assessments for Plastic and Paper Bags

Life Cycle Assessment Stage	Plastic Bag	Paper Bag
Raw Materials	Crude oil	Timber
Manufacturing and Packaging	The compounds needed to make the plastic are extracted from crude oil by fractional distillation, followed by cracking and then polymerisation. Waste is reduced as the other fractions of crude oil have other uses.	Pulped timber is processed using lots of energy. Lots of waste is made.
Using the Product	Can be reused. Can be used for other things as well as shopping, for example bin liners.	Usually only used once.
Product Disposal	Recyclable but not biodegradable and will take up space in landfill and pollute land.	Biodegradable, non-toxic and can be recycled.

Life cycle assessments have shown that even though plastic bags aren't biodegradable, they take less energy to make and have a longer lifespan than paper bags, so may be less harmful to the environment.

There are Problems with Life Cycle Assessments

1) The use of energy, some natural resources and the amount of certain types of waste produced by a product over it's lifetime can be easily quantified. But the effect of some pollutants is harder to give a numerical value to. E.g. it's difficult to apply a value to the negative visual effects of plastic bags in the environment compared to paper ones.
2) So, producing an LCA is not an objective method as it takes into account the values of the person carrying out the assessment. This means LCAs can be biased.
3) Selective LCAs, which only show some of the impacts of a product on the environment can also be biased as they can be written to deliberately support the claims of a company, in order to give them positive advertising.

Need exercise? Go life-cycling then...

In the exam you may be asked to evaluate the use of different materials for a particular product, using an LCA.

Q1 What are the four stages that need to be considered to conduct a life cycle assessment? [4 marks]

Potable Water

We all need safe drinking water. The <u>way</u> that water's made safe depends on <u>local conditions</u>.

Potable Water is Water You Can Drink

1) Potable water is water that's been <u>treated</u> or is naturally <u>safe</u> for <u>humans to drink</u> — it's <u>essential for life</u>.

2) Chemists wouldn't call it <u>pure</u>, though. Pure water <u>only</u> contains H_2O molecules whereas <u>potable water</u> can contain lots of other <u>dissolved substances</u>.

3) The important thing is that the <u>levels</u> of <u>dissolved salts</u> aren't <u>too high</u>, that it has a <u>pH</u> between <u>6.5 and 8.5</u> and also that there aren't any nasties (like <u>bacteria</u> or other <u>microbes</u>) swimming around in it.

The Way that Potable Water is Produced Depends on Where You Are

1) Rainwater is a type of <u>fresh water</u>. Fresh water is water that doesn't have much dissolved in it.

2) When it rains, water can either collect as <u>surface water</u> (in lakes, rivers and reservoirs) or as <u>groundwater</u> (in rocks called <u>aquifers</u> that trap water underground).

3) In the UK, the <u>source</u> of fresh water used depends on <u>location</u>. Surface water tends to <u>dry up</u> first, so in <u>warm areas</u>, e.g. the south-east, <u>most</u> of the domestic water supply comes from <u>groundwater</u>.

4) Even though it only has <u>low levels</u> of dissolved substances, water from these <u>fresh water sources</u> still needs to be <u>treated</u> to make it <u>safe</u> before it can be used. This process includes:

> - <u>Filtration</u> — a <u>wire mesh</u> screens out large twigs etc, and then <u>gravel</u> and <u>sand beds</u> filter out any other <u>solid bits</u>.
> - <u>Sterilisation</u> — the water is <u>sterilised</u> to kill any harmful <u>bacteria</u> or <u>microbes</u>. This can be done by bubbling <u>chlorine gas</u> through it or by using <u>ozone</u> or <u>ultraviolet light</u>.

mesh

sand and gravel filtration

sterilisation

5) In some very <u>dry</u> countries, e.g. Kuwait, there's <u>not enough</u> surface or groundwater and instead <u>sea water</u> must be treated by <u>desalination</u> to provide potable water.

6) <u>Distillation</u> can be used to <u>desalinate</u> sea water. Here's how you can test and distil water in the lab:

Chemicals can also be added to the water supply, such as fluoride (which is good for teeth). This is controversial, because people aren't given any choice over whether they consume them or not.

PRACTICAL

> - First, test the pH of the water using a <u>pH meter</u>. If the pH is too high or too low, you'll need to <u>neutralise</u> it. You can do this with a <u>titration</u> (see p.52), but use a pH meter to tell you when the solution's neutral, rather than an indicator, as this won't contaminate the water.
> - You should also <u>test</u> the water for the presence of <u>sodium chloride</u> (the main salt in seawater). To test for sodium ions, do a <u>flame test</u> on a small sample (see p.89). If sodium ions are present the flame will turn <u>yellow</u>. To test for chloride ions, take another sample of your water and add a few drops of <u>dilute nitric acid</u>, followed by a few drops of <u>silver nitrate solution</u>. If chloride ions are present, a <u>white precipitate</u> will form.
> - To distil the water, pour the salty water into a distillation apparatus, like the one on p.18. <u>Heat</u> the flask from below. The water will <u>boil</u> and form steam, leaving any dissolved salts in the flask. The steam will <u>condense</u> back to liquid water in the condenser and can be collected as it runs out.
> - Then, <u>retest</u> the distilled water for sodium chloride to check that it has been removed. Also retest the <u>pH</u> of the water with a pH meter to check that it's neutral (has a pH of 7).

7) Sea water can also be treated by processes that use <u>membranes</u> — like <u>reverse osmosis</u>. The salty water is passed through a <u>membrane</u> that only allows water molecules to pass through. Ions and larger molecules are <u>trapped</u> by the membrane so <u>separated</u> from the water.

8) Both of distillation and reverse osmosis need <u>loads of energy</u>, so they're really <u>expensive</u> and <u>not practical</u> for producing <u>large quantities</u> of fresh water.

Potable water — nothing to do with gardening...

Distilling salty water could be useful if you ever end up stranded on a desert island. Oh, and for your exams too.

Q1   Describe the steps you could take to treat water from a groundwater source to make it potable.   [2 marks]

Waste Water Treatment

It might not be pretty, but dealing with our waste is really important to ensure that we don't <u>pollute</u> the natural environment — it also means that we can access <u>nice clean water</u>. Super.

Waste Water Comes from Lots of Different Sources

1) We use water for lots of things at home — like <u>having a bath</u>, going to the <u>toilet</u>, doing the <u>washing-up</u>, etc. When you flush this water down the drain, it goes into the <u>sewers</u> and towards <u>sewage treatment plants</u>.

2) <u>Agricultural systems</u> also produce a lot of waste water including <u>nutrient run-off</u> from fields and <u>slurry</u> from animal farms.

3) Sewage from <u>domestic</u> or <u>agricultural</u> sources has to be <u>treated</u> to remove any <u>organic matter</u> and <u>harmful microbes</u> before it can be put <u>back</u> into freshwater sources like <u>rivers</u> or <u>lakes</u>. Otherwise it would make them very <u>polluted</u> and would pose <u>health risks</u>.

4) <u>Industrial processes</u> such as the Haber Process (see the next page) also produce a lot of waste water that has to be <u>collected</u> and <u>treated</u>.

5) As well as <u>organic matter</u>, industrial waste water can also contain <u>harmful chemicals</u> — so it has to undergo <u>additional stages</u> of treatment before it is safe to release it into the environment.

Sewage Treatment Happens in Several Stages

Some of the <u>processes</u> involved in treating waste water at sewage treatment plants include:

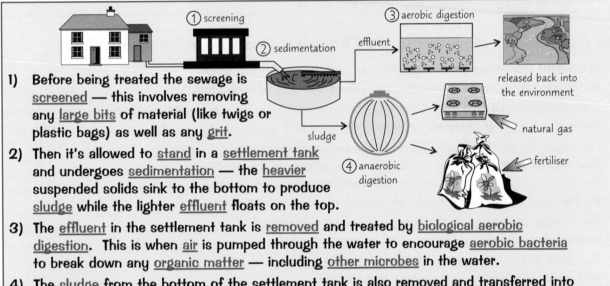

1) Before being treated the sewage is <u>screened</u> — this involves removing any <u>large bits</u> of material (like twigs or plastic bags) as well as any <u>grit</u>.

2) Then it's allowed to <u>stand</u> in a <u>settlement tank</u> and undergoes <u>sedimentation</u> — the <u>heavier</u> suspended solids sink to the bottom to produce <u>sludge</u> while the lighter <u>effluent</u> floats on the top.

3) The <u>effluent</u> in the settlement tank is <u>removed</u> and treated by <u>biological aerobic digestion</u>. This is when <u>air</u> is pumped through the water to encourage <u>aerobic bacteria</u> to break down any <u>organic matter</u> — including <u>other microbes</u> in the water.

4) The <u>sludge</u> from the bottom of the settlement tank is also removed and transferred into large <u>tanks</u>. Here it gets <u>broken down</u> by bacteria in a process called <u>anaerobic digestion</u>.

5) Anaerobic digestion breaks down the organic matter in the sludge, releasing <u>methane gas</u> in the process. The methane gas can be used as an <u>energy source</u> and the remaining digested waste can be used as a <u>fertiliser</u>.

Aerobic just means with oxygen, whereas <u>anaerobic</u> means without oxygen.

6) For waste water containing <u>toxic substances</u>, additional stages of treatment may involve adding <u>chemicals</u> (e.g. to precipitate metals), <u>UV radiation</u> or using <u>membranes</u>.

Sewage treatment requires <u>more processes</u> than treating <u>fresh water</u> but uses <u>less energy</u> than the <u>desalination</u> of <u>salt water</u>, so could be used as an alternative in areas where there's not much fresh water. For example, <u>Singapore</u> is treating waste water and recycling it back into drinking supplies. However, people don't like the idea of drinking water that used to be sewage.

Is it just me, or does this page stink? Phew...

Modern sewage systems have done wonders to make life in developed countries much less... well... smelly.

Q1   List three stages of treatment that domestic sewage undergoes at a sewage treatment plant.   [3 marks]

The Haber Process

This is an important industrial process. It produces <u>ammonia</u> (NH$_3$), which is used to make <u>fertilisers</u>.

Nitrogen and Hydrogen are Needed to Make Ammonia

The <u>Haber process</u> is used to make <u>ammonia</u> from hydrogen and nitrogen using the following reaction:

$$N_{2\,(g)} + 3H_{2\,(g)} \rightleftharpoons 2NH_{3\,(g)} \quad (+ \text{heat})$$
nitrogen   hydrogen   ammonia

This reaction is well suited for an industrial scale as the reactants aren't too <u>difficult</u> or <u>expensive</u> to obtain.

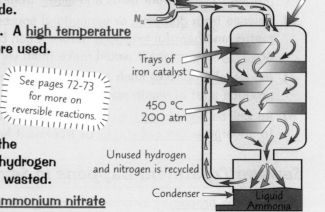

1) The <u>nitrogen</u> is obtained easily from the <u>air</u>, which is <u>78% nitrogen</u>.

2) The <u>hydrogen</u> mainly comes from reacting methane (from <u>natural gas</u>) with steam to form hydrogen and carbon dioxide.

3) The reactant gases are passed over an <u>iron catalyst</u>. A <u>high temperature</u> (450 °C) and a <u>high pressure</u> (200 atmospheres) are used.

4) Because the reaction is <u>reversible</u> (it occurs in both directions), some of the ammonia produced <u>converts back</u> into hydrogen and nitrogen again. It eventually reaches a <u>dynamic equilibrium</u>.

   See pages 72-73 for more on reversible reactions.

5) The ammonia is formed as a <u>gas</u>, but as it cools in the <u>condenser</u> it <u>liquefies</u> and is removed. The unused hydrogen (H$_2$), and nitrogen, (N$_2$), are <u>recycled</u>, so nothing is wasted.

6) The ammonia produced can then be used to make <u>ammonium nitrate</u> — a very nitrogen-rich <u>fertiliser</u> (see next page).

The Reaction is Reversible, So There's a Compromise to be Made

1) You might remember from page 68 that certain conditions, such as the temperature and pressure, can affect the <u>rate</u> of a reaction.

2) These factors can also affect the <u>position of equilibrium</u> for a <u>reversible</u> reaction — and sometimes there is a <u>trade-off</u> between <u>increasing the rate</u> and <u>maximising the yield</u> (see page 49) of a reaction.

3) For example, the <u>forward</u> reaction in the Haber process is <u>exothermic</u>. That means that <u>increasing</u> the temperature will move the equilibrium the <u>wrong way</u> — away from ammonia and towards nitrogen and hydrogen. So the <u>yield</u> of ammonia would be <u>greater</u> at <u>lower</u> temperatures.

   For more on factors that affect the position of equilibrium, see page 73.

4) The trouble is, <u>lower temperatures</u> mean a <u>slower</u> rate of reaction (and so equilibrium is reached more slowly).

5) The 450 °C is a <u>compromise</u> between <u>maximum yield</u> and <u>speed of reaction</u>. It's better to wait just 20 seconds for a 10% yield than to have to wait 60 seconds for a 20% yield.

   Graph showing the effect of pressure on rate of reaction

   Amount of product evolved

   As the pressure increases, the line gets steeper — so the rate increases.
   ③ 200 atmospheres
   ② 100 atmospheres
   ① 50 atmospheres

   As the pressure increases, the yield of ammonia also increases.

   Time

6) Higher pressures move the <u>position of equilibrium</u> towards the <u>products</u> since there are <u>four</u> molecules of gas on the <u>left-hand</u> side for every <u>two</u> molecules on the <u>right</u>. So increasing <u>pressure</u> maximises the percentage yield. It also increases the <u>rate</u> of reaction.

7) So the pressure is set as <u>high as possible</u>, without making the process <u>too expensive</u> to or <u>dangerous</u> to build and maintain. Hence the <u>200 atmospheres</u> operating pressure.

8) And finally, the <u>iron catalyst</u> makes the reaction go faster, but <u>doesn't affect</u> the yield.

You need to learn this stuff — go on, Haber go at it...

The trickiest bit of this page is remembering that temperature is raised not for a better equilibrium, but for speed. Remember that industries have to consider costs — so a higher pressure may give a better yield, but it's not cheap.

Q1   What are the industrial conditions used in the Haber process and why?   [3 marks]

NPK Fertilisers

Fertilisers allow us to keep growing crops on the same land every year — thanks to our old friend ammonia.

NPK Fertilisers *Provide Plants with the Essential Elements for Growth*

1) Farmers used to use manure to fertilise fields. Formulated fertilisers are better as they're more widely available, easier to use, don't smell and have just enough of each nutrient so more crops can be grown.

2) The three main essential elements in fertilisers are nitrogen, phosphorus and potassium. If plants don't get enough of these elements, their growth and life processes are affected. These elements may be missing from the soil if they've been used up by a previous crop.

3) Fertilisers replace these missing elements or provide more of them. This helps to increase the crop yield, as the crops can grow faster and bigger. For example, fertilisers add more nitrogen to plant proteins, which makes the plants grow faster — increasing productivity.

There's more on formulations on p.86.

4) NPK fertilisers are formulations containing salts of nitrogen (N), phosphorus (P) and potassium (K) (hence, "NPK") in the right percentages of the elements.

Ammonia is Used to Produce Nitrogen-Containing Compounds

1) Ammonia can be reacted with oxygen and water in a series of reactions to make nitric acid.

2) You can also react ammonia with acids, including nitric acid, to get ammonium salts.

3) Ammonia and nitric acid react together to produce ammonium nitrate — this is an especially good compound to use in a fertiliser because it has nitrogen from two sources.

$$NH_{3\,(aq)} + HNO_{3\,(aq)} \rightarrow NH_4NO_{3\,(aq)}$$
Ammonia + Nitric acid → Ammonium nitrate

4) This reaction is carried out differently in industry to how it is done in the lab. You may be asked to compare differences between the different methods in your exam:

In Industry

The reaction is carried out in giant vats, at high concentrations resulting in a very exothermic reaction. The heat released is used to evaporate water from the mixture to make a very concentrated ammonium nitrate product.

If you get asked to compare reactions in the exams, you'll be given all the details you need.

In the Lab

The reaction is carried out on a much smaller scale by titration and crystallisation. The reactants are at a much lower concentration than in industry, so less heat is produced by the reaction and it's safer for a person to carry it out. After the titration, the mixture then needs to be crystallised to give pure ammonium nitrate crystals. Crystallisation isn't used in industry because it's very slow.

For how to carry out a titration or crystallisation have a look at p.52 and p.17.

Phosphate and Potassium are Sourced from Mined Compounds

1) Potassium chloride and potassium sulphate can be mined and used as a source of potassium.

2) Phosphate rock is also mined. However, because the phosphate salts in the rock are insoluble, plants can't use them as nutrients.

3) Reacting phosphate rock with a number of different types of acids produces soluble phosphates:

- Reaction with nitric acid produces phosphoric acid and calcium nitrate.
- Reaction with sulfuric acid produces calcium sulfate and calcium phosphate (this mixture is known as single superphosphate).
- Reaction with phosphoric acid only produces calcium phosphate (the product of this reaction can be called triple superphosphate).

There's nowt wrong wi' just spreadin' muck on it...

Not the most thrilling of pages, I'm afraid. Just loads of reactions for you to learn... It's important stuff, though.

Q1 Suggest a source of potassium in an NPK fertiliser. [1 mark]

Revision Questions for Topic 10

Topic 10 — done. Now is as good a time as any to have another read back over the section.
- Try these questions and <u>tick off each one</u> when you <u>get it right</u>.
- When you've done <u>all the questions</u> under a heading and are <u>completely happy</u> with it, tick it off.

Properties and Uses of Materials (p.96-97) ☑

1) How is soda-lime glass made? ☑
2) Give three examples of composite materials. ☑
3) Describe the differences in the properties of low density poly(ethene) and high density poly(ethene). ☑
4) Name two elements that can be added to iron to make stainless steel. ☑
5) What two metals is bronze made of? ☑
6) Give two uses of brass. ☑

Corrosion (p.98) ☐

7) What two substances does iron react with when it rusts? ☑
8) Aluminium objects can corrode. Why is aluminium not completely destroyed by corrosion? ☑
9) Suggest three ways of making a barrier that can be used to protect an iron object from rusting. ☑
10) Suggest one metal that can be used in the sacrificial method to prevent rusting. ☑

Chemistry and Sustainability (p.99-101) ☐

11) Give two examples of renewable resources. ☑
12) Suggest one way in which chemistry is improving sustainability. ☑
13) State two methods that can be used to extract copper from low grade ores. ☑
14) Other than recycling, how can glass bottles be used in a sustainable way? ☑
15) What do life cycle assessments (LCA) do? ☑

Potable Water and Waste Water Treatment (p.102-103) ☐

16) What is potable water? ☑
17) Suggest a source of fresh water. ☑
18) Describe how you could distil seawater in the lab. ☑
19) What other method could you use for making sea water potable? ☑
20) Name three different sources of waste water. ☑
21) Why is it important to treat waste water before releasing it into the environment? ☑
22) What type of waste water could contain harmful chemicals? ☑
23) What two products can be obtained by the anaerobic digestion of sewage sludge? ☑

The Haber Process (p.104) ☐

24) What is the balanced symbol equation for the Haber process? ☑
25) From what source is the hydrogen used in the Haber process obtained? ☑
26) What happens to the unused hydrogen and nitrogen in the Haber process? ☑

NPK Fertilisers (p.105) ☐

27) What three elements are present in NPK fertilisers? ☑
28) What substances can be reacted with each other to produce the following:
   a) ammonium nitrate, b) phosphoric acid and calcium nitrate, c) calcium phosphate only? ☑

Practical Techniques

Safety specs out and lab coats on, it's time to find out about the skills you'll need in <u>experiments</u>. Finally time to look like a real scientist... hurrah! But you also need to know about this stuff in your exams... boooo...

Solids Should Be Measured Using a Balance

1) To weigh a solid, start by putting the <u>container</u> you're weighing your substance <u>into</u> on the <u>balance</u>.

2) Set the balance to exactly <u>zero</u> and then start weighing out your substance.

3) It's <u>no good</u> carefully weighing out your solid if it's not all transferred to your reaction vessel
— the amount in the <u>reaction vessel</u> won't be the same as your measurement. Here are a couple of methods you can use to make sure that none gets left in your weighing container...

- If you're <u>dissolving</u> a solid in a solvent to make a <u>solution</u>, you could <u>wash</u> any remaining solid into the new container using the <u>solvent</u>.
- You could set the balance to zero <u>before</u> you put your <u>weighing container</u> on the balance. Then <u>reweigh</u> the weighing container <u>after</u> you've transferred the solid. Use the <u>difference in mass</u> to work out <u>exactly</u> how much solid you added to your experiment.

Three Ways to Measure Liquids

There are a few methods you might use to measure the volume of a liquid. Whichever method you use, always read the volume from the <u>bottom of the meniscus</u> (the curved upper surface of the liquid) when it's at <u>eye level</u>.

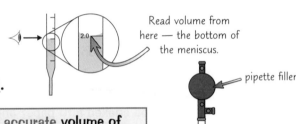

Read volume from here — the bottom of the meniscus.

pipette filler

<u>Pipettes</u> are long, narrow tubes that are used to suck up an <u>accurate</u> volume of liquid and <u>transfer</u> it to another container. A <u>pipette filler</u> attached to the end of the pipette is used so that you can <u>safely control</u> the amount of liquid you're drawing up. Pipettes are often <u>calibrated</u> to allow for the fact that the last drop of liquid stays in the pipette when the liquid is ejected. This reduces <u>transfer errors</u>.

<u>Burettes</u> measure from top to bottom (so when they're filled to the top of the scale, the scale reads zero). They have a tap at the bottom which you can use to release the liquid into another container (you can even release it drop by drop). To use a burette, take an <u>initial reading</u>, and once you've released as much liquid as you want, take a <u>final reading</u>. The <u>difference</u> between the readings tells you <u>how much</u> liquid you used.

Burettes are used a lot for titrations. There's loads more about titrations on page 52.

<u>Measuring cylinders</u> are the most common way to measure out a liquid. They come in all different <u>sizes</u>. Make sure you choose one that's the right size for the measurement you want to make. It's no good using a huge 1000 cm³ cylinder to measure out 2 cm³ of a liquid — the graduations will be too big, and you'll end up with <u>massive errors</u>. It'd be much better to use one that measures up to 10 cm³.

If you only want a couple of drops of liquid, and don't need it to be accurately measured, you can use a dropping pipette to transfer it. For example, this is how you'd add a couple of drops of indicator into a mixture.

Gas Syringes Measure Gas Volumes

Gases can be measured with a gas syringe. They should be measured at <u>room temperature and pressure</u> as the <u>volume</u> of a gas <u>changes</u> with temperature and pressure. You should also use a gas syringe that's the <u>right size</u> for the measurement you're making. Before you use the syringe, you should make sure it's completely sealed and that the plunger moves smoothly.

Practical Techniques

Measure Temperature Accurately

You can use a <u>thermometer</u> to measure the temperature of a substance:

1) Make sure the <u>bulb</u> of your thermometer is <u>completely submerged</u> in any mixture you're measuring.

2) If you're taking an initial reading, you should wait for the temperature to <u>stabilise</u> first.

3) Read your measurement off the <u>scale</u> on a thermometer at <u>eye level</u> to make sure it's correct.

You May Have to Measure the Time Taken for a Change

1) You should use a <u>stopwatch</u> to <u>time</u> experiments. These measure to the nearest <u>0.1 s</u> so are <u>sensitive</u>.

2) Always make sure you <u>start</u> and <u>stop</u> the stopwatch at exactly the right time. For example, if you're investigating the rate of an experiment, you should start timing at the <u>exact moment</u> you mix the reagents and start the reaction. If you're measuring the time taken for a precipitate to form, you should watch the reaction like a hawk so you can <u>stop</u> timing the moment it goes cloudy.

Measure pH to Find Out How Acidic or Alkaline a Solution Is

You need to be able to decide the best method for measuring pH, depending on what your experiment is.

1) <u>Indicators</u> are dyes that <u>change colour</u> depending on whether they're in an <u>acid</u> or an <u>alkali</u>. You use them by adding a couple of drops of the indicator to the solution you're interested in. They're useful for titration reactions, when you want to find the point at which a solution is neutralised.

2) <u>Universal indicator</u> is a <u>mixture</u> of indicators that changes colour <u>gradually</u> as pH changes. It doesn't show a <u>sudden</u> colour change. It's useful for <u>estimating</u> the pH of a solution based on its colour.

3) Indicators can be soaked into <u>paper</u> and strips of this paper can be used for testing pH. If you use a dropping pipette to spot a small amount of a solution onto some indicator paper, it will <u>change colour</u> depending on the pH of the solution.

> <u>Litmus paper</u> turns <u>red</u> in acidic conditions and <u>blue</u> in basic conditions. <u>Universal indicator paper</u> can be used to <u>estimate</u> the pH based on its colour.

4) Indicator paper is useful when you <u>don't</u> want to change the colour of <u>all</u> of the substance, or if the substance is <u>already</u> coloured so might <u>obscure</u> the colour of the indicator. You can also hold a piece of <u>damp indicator paper</u> in a <u>gas sample</u> to test its pH.

5) <u>pH probes</u> are attached to pH meters which have a <u>digital display</u> that gives a <u>numerical</u> value for the pH of a solution. They're used to give an <u>accurate value</u> of pH.

There's loads more about pH on page 51.

Be Careful When You Handle or Mix Substances

1) There are lots of hazards in chemistry experiments, so <u>before</u> you start any experiment, you should read any <u>safety precautions</u> to do with your method or the chemicals you're using.

2) The substances used in chemical reactions are often <u>hazardous</u>. For example, they might catch fire easily (they're flammable), or they might irritate or burn your skin if you come into contact with them.

3) Whenever you're doing an experiment, you should wear a <u>lab coat</u>, <u>safety goggles</u> and <u>gloves</u>.

4) Always be careful that the chemicals you're using aren't flammable before you go lighting any Bunsen burners, and make sure you're working in an area that's <u>well ventilated</u>.

5) If you're doing an experiment that might produce nasty <u>gases</u> (such as chlorine), you should carry out the experiment in a <u>fume hood</u> so that the gas can't escape out into the room you're working in.

6) Never directly touch any chemicals (even if you're wearing gloves). Use a <u>spatula</u> to transfer <u>solids</u> between containers. Carefully <u>pour</u> liquids between different containers, using a <u>funnel</u> to avoid spillages.

7) Be careful when you're <u>mixing</u> chemicals, as a reaction might occur. If you're <u>diluting</u> a liquid, add the <u>concentrated substance</u> to the <u>water</u> (not the other way around) or the mixture could get very <u>hot</u>.

The Tempipettes and MacBurette — Shakespeare for chemists...

It's no good throwing chemicals around willy nilly and calling it an experiment. To make sure your results are reproducible, so can be trusted by other scientists, you have to make sure all your measurements are accurate.

Setting Up Equipment

Setting up the equipment for an experiment correctly is <u>just as important</u> as making accurate measurements.

To Collect Gases, the System Needs to be Sealed

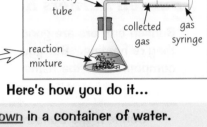

delivery tube

reaction mixture

collected gas

gas syringe

1) There are times when you might want to <u>collect</u> the gas produced by a reaction. For example, to investigate the <u>rate</u> of reaction.

2) The most accurate way to measure the volume of a gas that's been produced is to collect it in a <u>gas syringe</u> (see page 107).

3) You could also collect it by <u>displacing water</u> from a measuring cylinder. Here's how you do it...

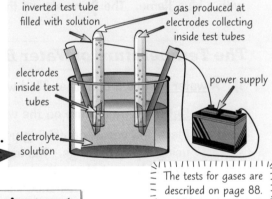

delivery tube

reaction mixture

collected gas

measuring cylinder filled with water and upturned in a beaker of water

- Fill a <u>measuring cylinder</u> with <u>water</u>, and carefully place it <u>upside down</u> in a container of water. Record the <u>initial level</u> of the water in the measuring cylinder.

- Position a <u>delivery tube</u> coming <u>from</u> the reaction vessel so that it's <u>inside</u> the measuring cylinder, pointing upwards. Any gas that's produced will pass <u>through</u> the delivery tube and <u>into</u> the <u>measuring cylinder</u>. As the gas enters the measuring cylinder, the <u>water</u> is <u>pushed out</u>.

- Record the <u>level of water</u> in the measuring cylinder and use this value, along with your <u>initial value</u>, to calculate the <u>volume</u> of gas produced.

If the delivery tube is underneath the measuring cylinder rather than inside it then some of the gas might escape out into the air.

4) This method is <u>less accurate</u> than using a gas syringe to measure the volume of gas produced. This is because some gases can <u>dissolve</u> in water, so less gas ends up in the measuring cylinder than is <u>actually produced</u>.

5) If you just want to <u>collect</u> a sample to test (and don't need to know the volume), you can collect it over water, as above, using a <u>test tube</u>. Once the test tube is full of gas, stopper it to store the gas for later.

You May Have to Identify the Products of Electrolysis

There's more about electrolysis on p.58-59.

1) When you electrolyse an <u>aqueous solution</u>, the products of electrolysis will depend on how reactive the ions in the solution are compared to the H^+ and OH^- ions that come from water.

2) At the <u>cathode</u> you'll either get a <u>pure metal</u> coating the electrode or bubbles of <u>hydrogen gas</u>.

3) At the <u>anode</u>, you'll get bubbles of <u>oxygen gas</u> unless a <u>halide ion</u> is present, when you'll get the <u>halogen</u>.

4) You may have to predict and identify what's been made in an electrolysis experiment. To do this, you need to be able to <u>set up the equipment</u> so that you can <u>collect</u> any gas that's produced. The easiest way to collect the gas is in a <u>test tube</u>.

5) Here's how to set up the equipment...

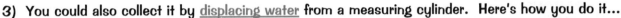

inverted test tube filled with solution

gas produced at electrodes collecting inside test tubes

electrodes inside test tubes

power supply

electrolyte solution

The tests for gases are described on page 88.

Make Sure You Can Draw Diagrams of Your Equipment

When you're writing out a <u>method</u> for your experiment, it's always a good idea to draw a <u>labelled diagram</u> showing how your apparatus will be <u>set up</u>. The easiest way to do this is to use a scientific drawing, where each piece of apparatus is drawn as if you're looking at its <u>cross-section</u>.

For example:

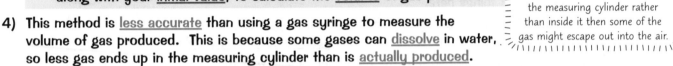

beaker   test tube   tripod   heat-proof mat   gauze   Bunsen burner

The pieces of glassware are drawn without tops so they aren't sealed. If you want to draw a closed system, remember to draw a bung in the top.

I set up my equipment — they had a blind date at the cinema...

Being a dab hand at setting up experiments won't just make your investigations more reliable. You might also be asked to comment on how an experiment's been set up in the exam. So best get learning. You'll thank me for it...

Heating Substances

Heating a reaction isn't as simple as wrapping it up in a lumpy wool jumper and a stripy scarf.
There's more than one way to do it, and you need to be able to decide on the best, and the safest, method.

Bunsen Burners Have a Naked Flame

Bunsen burners are good for heating things quickly. You can easily adjust how strongly
they're heating. But you need to be careful not to use them if you're heating flammable
compounds as the flame means the substance would be at risk of catching fire.

Here's how to use a Bunsen burner...

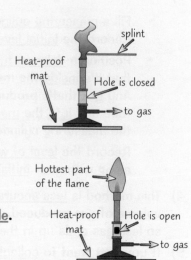

- Connect the Bunsen burner to a gas tap, and check that the hole is closed. Place it on a heat-proof mat.
- Light a splint and hold it over the Bunsen burner. Now, turn on the gas. The Bunsen burner should light with a yellow flame.
- The more open the hole is, the more strongly the Bunsen burner will heat your substance. Open the hole to the amount you want. As you open the hole more, the flame should turn more blue.
- The hottest part of the flame is just above the blue cone, so you should heat things here.
- If your Bunsen burner is alight but not heating anything, make sure you close the hole so that the flame becomes yellow and clearly visible.
- If you're heating something so that the container (e.g. a test tube) is in the flame, you should hold the vessel at the top, furthest away from the substance (and so the flame) using a pair of tongs.
- If you're heating something over the flame (e.g. an evaporating dish), you should put a tripod and gauze over the Bunsen burner before you light it, and place the vessel on this.

You'd use a Bunsen burner to carry out flame tests to identify metal ions in a compound (see page 89).
A sample of the compound is placed on a metal wire that you hold just above the cone of a Bunsen burner
with a blue flame. The flame should then change colour depending on what metal ion is in the sample.

The Temperature of Water Baths & Electric Heaters Can Be Set

1) A water bath is a container filled with water that can be heated to a specific temperature.

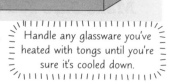

- Set the temperature on the water bath, and allow the water to heat up.
- Place the vessel containing your substance in the water bath using a pair of tongs. The level of the water outside the vessel should be just above the level of the substance inside the vessel. The substance will then be warmed to the same temperature as the water.

As the substance in the vessel is surrounded by water, the heating is very even.
Water boils at 100 °C though, so you can't use a water bath to heat something
to a higher temperature than this — the water won't get hot enough.

Handle any glassware you've heated with tongs until you're sure it's cooled down.

2) Electric heaters are often made up of a metal plate that can be heated to a certain temperature.
The vessel containing the substance you want to heat is placed on top of the hot plate. You can heat
substances to higher temperatures than you can in a water bath but, as the vessel is only heated from
below, you'll usually have to stir the substance inside to make sure it's heated evenly.

A bath and an electric heater — how I spend my January nights...

You know, I used to have a chemistry teacher who'd play power ballads when the Bunsen burners were alight and
sway at the front of the class like he was at a gig. You think I made that up, but it's true.

Practical Skills

Answers

p.12 — Atoms
Q1 protons = atomic number = 7 *[1 mark]*
electrons = protons = 7 *[1 mark]*
neutrons = mass number – atomic number
= 14 – 7 = 7 *[1 mark]*

p.13 — Elements
Q1 E.g. it's the number of protons in an atom that determines what type of atom it is, so if all the atoms have the same number of protons then the substance is an element *[1 mark]*.
Q2 protons = 26 *[1 mark]*
neutrons = 56 – 26 = 30 *[1 mark]*

p.14 — Compounds
Q1 (2 × Na) + (1 × C) + (3 × O) = 6 *[1 mark]*
Q2 calcium chloride *[1 mark]*
Calcium and chlorine *[1 mark]*.

p.15 — Chemical Equations
Q1 $2Fe + 3Cl_2 \rightarrow 2FeCl_3$ *[1 mark]*
Q2 a) water → hydrogen + oxygen *[1 mark]*
b) $2H_2O \rightarrow 2H_2 + O_2$
[1 mark for correct products and reactants, 1 mark for being balanced correctly]

p.16 — Mixtures and Chromatography
Q1 The pen ink might dissolve in the solvent and rise up the filter paper *[1 mark]*.

p.17 — More Separation Techniques
Q1 Pour the copper sulfate solution into an evaporating dish and slowly heat the solution until crystals start to form or some of the solvent has evaporated *[1 mark]*. Leave the dish to cool until crystals form *[1 mark]*. Filter *[1 mark]* and then dry the crystals using a desiccator/drying oven *[1 mark]*.

p.18 — Distillation
Q1 Ethanol *[1 mark]*. Ethanol has the second lowest boiling point and will be collected once all the methanol has been distilled off and the temperature increased *[1 mark]*.

p.19 — The History of the Atom
Q1 In the plum pudding model, the atom is a ball of positive charge with electrons spread throughout it *[1 mark]*.
Q2 If the plum pudding model was correct you would expect most of the alpha particles to have passed through the foil or only to have been deflected slightly *[1 mark]*. The actual deflections of the particles suggests that atoms contain a small nucleus where the positive charge is concentrated *[1 mark]*.

p.20 — Electronic Structure
Q1 2,8,3 or

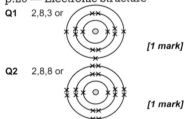

[1 mark]

Q2 2,8,8 or

[1 mark]

p.21 — Development of the Periodic Table
Q1 By relative atomic mass *[1 mark]*.
Q2 E.g. he left gaps in order to keep elements with similar properties in the same group *[1 mark]*. He switched the order of elements based on their properties, even if their atomic masses were no longer in order. *[1 mark]*.

p.22 — The Modern Periodic Table
Q1 2 *[1 mark]*
Q2 Both chlorine and bromine are in Group 7 and so have the same number of electrons in their outer shell *[1 mark]*.
Q3 E.g. potassium forms 1+ ions as it's in the same group as sodium so will react in a similar way *[1 mark]*.

p.23 — Metals and Non-Metals
Q1 Any three from: e.g. metals tend to be strong / good conductors of heat / good at conducting electricity / malleable / high melting/boiling temperatures *[1 mark for each]*.

p.24 — Group 1 Elements
Q1 As you go further down the group the outer electron is further away from the nucleus *[1 mark]*. This means the attraction between the nucleus and the electron decreases so is more easily removed resulting in an increase in reactivity *[1 mark]*.

p.25 — Group 7 Elements
Q1 Bromine would displace iodine from sodium iodide *[1 mark]* because bromine is more reactive than iodine *[1 mark]*.
Q2 Halogens react by gaining electrons to make a full outer-shell *[1 mark]*. As you go further down the group the outer electrons are further away so there is less attraction between them and the nucleus *[1 mark]*. This means electrons are harder to gain so they become less reactive *[1 mark]*.

p.26 — Group 0 Elements
Q1 Xenon has a higher boiling point than neon *[1 mark]*.
Q2 Argon has a full outer-shell *[1 mark]* so is electronically stable and does not readily lose or gain electrons *[1 mark]*.

p.28 — Formation of Ions
Q1 Noble gas electronic structures have a full shell of outer electrons *[1 mark]*, which is a very stable structure *[1 mark]*.
Q2 a) 1– *[1 mark]*
b) 2+ *[1 mark]*
c) 1+ *[1 mark]*

p.29 — Ionic Bonding
Q1 Each sodium atom loses an electron to form an Na^+ ion *[1 mark]*. Each chlorine atom gains an electron to form a Cl^- ion *[1 mark]*. The oppositely charged ions are attracted to each other by electrostatic attraction *[1 mark]*.
Q2

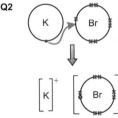

[1 mark for arrow showing electron transferred from potassium to bromine, 1 mark for correct outer shell electron configurations (with or without inner shells), 1 mark for correct charges]

p.30 — Ionic Compounds
Q1 a) It will have a high melting point *[1 mark]* because a lot of energy is needed to break the strong attraction between the ions/the strong ionic bonds *[1 mark]*.
b) When melted, the ions are free to move, so they can carry an electric current *[1 mark]*.
c) The compound contains caesium and chloride ions. Caesium is in Group 1 so forms 1+ ions *[1 mark]*, and chlorine is in Group 7 so forms 1– ions *[1 mark]*. The charges balance with one of each ion, so the empirical formula is CsCl *[1 mark]*.

p.31 — Covalent Bonding
Q1

[1 mark for 3 shared pairs of electrons, 1 mark for correct number of electrons in outer shell of each atom (with or without inner shells on nitrogen)]

p.32 — Simple Molecular Substances
Q1 The intermolecular forces between molecules of O_2 are weak and don't need much energy to break *[1 mark]*.
Q2 N_2 molecules aren't charged/There aren't any free electrons or ions *[1 mark]*.

p.33 — Polymers and Giant Covalent Structures
Q1 $(C_2H_3Cl)_n$ *[1 mark]*
Q2 To melt diamond you have to break the covalent bonds between atoms which are very strong *[1 mark]* but to melt poly(ethene) you only have to break the weaker intermolecular forces which needs less energy *[1 mark]*. So diamond has a higher melting point *[1 mark]*.

p.34 — Allotropes of Carbon
Q1 Any three from, e.g.: lubricants / catalysts / drug delivery / to strengthen materials *[1 mark for each, up to 3 marks]*

p.35 — Metallic Bonding
Q1 Copper is a good electrical conductor *[1 mark]* as it contains delocalised electrons which are able to carry an electrical current *[1 mark]*.
Q2 Pure copper would be too soft to use for a door hinge, but alloys are harder than pure metals, so are suitable *[1 mark]*.

p.36 — States of Matter
Q1 The gaseous state *[1 mark]*.

p.37 — Changing State
Q1 a) solid *[1 mark]*
b) liquid *[1 mark]*
c) liquid *[1 mark]*
d) gas *[1 mark]*

p.38 — Nanoparticles
Q1 Between 1 nm and 100 nm *[1 mark]*.
Q2 a) Surface area of one face
= 50 nm × 50 nm = 2500 nm^2
Total surface area = 6 × 2500 nm = 15 000 nm^2 *[1 mark]*
Volume = 50 nm × 50 nm × 50 nm
= 125 000 nm^3 *[1 mark]*
Surface area to volume ratio
= 15 000 nm^2 ÷ 125 000 nm^3
= 0.12 nm^{-1} *[1 mark]*
b) It would decrease *[1 mark]* by a factor of ten *[1 mark]*. (As the length of the sides has increased by a factor of ten).

p.39 — Uses of Nanoparticles
Q1 E.g. in electrical circuits for computer chips *[1 mark]*.
Q2 E.g. they might have long-term impacts on health *[1 mark]*.
Q3 Silver nanoparticles. They form a transparent layer, so the window will still be see-through *[1 mark]* and they conduct heat, so will be able to warm the window and melt the frost *[1 mark]*.

p.41 — Relative Formula Mass

Q1 a) A_r of H = 1 and A_r of O = 16
M_r of H_2O = (2 × 1) + 16 = 18 *[1 mark]*

b) A_r of Li = 7, A_r of O = 16 and A_r of H = 1
So M_r of LiOH = 7 + 16 + 1 = 24 *[1 mark]*

c) A_r of H = 1, A_r of S = 32 and A_r of O = 16
M_r of H_2SO_4 = (2 × 1) + 32 + (4 × 16) = 98 *[1 mark]*

Q2 A_r of K = 39, A_r of O = 16 and A_r of H = 1
M_r of KOH = 39 + 16 + 1 = 56 *[1 mark]*
$\frac{39}{56}$ × 100 = 70% *[1 mark]*

p.42 — The Mole

Q1 M_r of H_2O = 16 + (2 × 1) = 18 *[1 mark]*
number of moles = mass ÷ M_r
number of moles = 90 g ÷ 18 = 5 moles
[1 mark]

Q2 M_r of KBr = 39 + 80 = 119 *[1 mark]*
mass = number of moles × M_r
mass = 0.20 × 119 = 24 g *[1 mark]*

p.43 — Conservation of Mass

Q1 Total mass on the left hand side
= $M_r(H_2SO_4)$ + 2 × $M_r(NaOH)$
M_r of H_2SO_4 = (2 × 1) + 32 + (4 × 16) = 98
2 × M_r of NaOH = 2 × (23 + 16 + 1) = 80
So total mass on the left hand side = 98 + 80
= 178 *[2 marks for 178, 1 mark for either 98 or 80]*
Total mass on right hand side
= $M_r(Na_2SO_4)$ + 2 × $M_r(H_2O)$
M_r of Na_2SO_4 = (2 × 23) + 32 + (4 × 16) = 142
2 × M_r of H_2O = 2 × [(2 × 1) + 16] = 36
142 + 36 = 178 *[2 marks for 178, 1 mark for either 142 or 36]*
The total M_r on the left-hand side is equal to the total M_r on the right-hand side, so mass is conserved *[1 mark]*.

p.44 — The Mole and Equations

Q1 a) N_2: $\frac{84}{28}$ = 3.0 mol *[1 mark]*
H_2: $\frac{18}{2}$ = 9 mol *[1 mark]*
NH_3: $\frac{102}{17}$ = 6.0 mol *[1 mark]*

b) Divide by the smallest number of moles (3.0):
N_2: $\frac{3.0}{3.0}$ = 1 H_2: $\frac{9}{3.0}$ = 3 NH_3: $\frac{6.0}{3.0}$ = 2.0
[1 mark]
The balanced symbol equation is:
N_2 + 3H_2 → 2NH_3 *[1 mark]*

p.45 — Limiting Reactants

Q1 $M_r(KBr)$ = 119, $M_r(KCl)$ = 74.5 *[1 mark]*
No. of moles of KBr = 23.8 ÷ 119 = 0.200 mol *[1 mark]*
From the reaction equation, 2 moles of KBr react to form 2 moles of KCl. So 0.200 moles of KBr reacts to form 0.200 moles of KCl *[1 mark]*.
Mass KCl = 74.5 × 0.200 = 14.9 g *[1 mark]*

p.46 — Gases and Solutions

Q1 $M_r(N_2)$ = 2 × 14 = 28 *[1 mark]*
Volume = $\frac{3.5}{28}$ × 24 = 3.0 dm³ *[1 mark]*

p.47 — Concentration Calculations

Q1 Moles of KOH: 0.150 × (22.5 ÷ 1000)
= 0.003375 *[1 mark]*
From the reaction equation, 1 mole of KOH reacts with 1 mole of HNO_3, so 0.003375 mol of KOH reacts with 0.003375 mol of HNO_3 *[1 mark]*.
Concentration of HNO_3:
(0.003375) ÷ (25.0 ÷ 1000) = 0.135 mol/dm³ *[1 mark]*

p.48 — Atom Economy

Q1 a) Reaction B, because it only has one product / the atom economy is 100% *[1 mark]*.

b) Total mass of all reactants:
$M_r(NH_4Cl)$ = 14 + (4 × 1) + 35.5 = 53.5 *[1 mark]*
$M_r(CaO)$ = 40 + 16 = 56 *[1 mark]*
(2 × 53.5) + (2 × 56) = 219 *[1 mark]*
Total mass of desired product
= 2 × $M_r(NH_3)$ = 34 *[1 mark]*
Atom economy = $\frac{34}{219}$ × 100 = 16% *[1 mark]*

p.49 — Percentage Yield

Q1 $\frac{2.31}{2.72}$ × 100 = 84.9% *[1 mark]*

p.51 — Acids and Bases

Q1 red/orange *[1 mark]*
Q2 alkaline *[1 mark]*

p.52 — Titrations

Q1 The indicator will have just changed colour *[1 mark]*.

Q2 E.g. to increase the accuracy of your result *[1 mark]* and to spot any anomalous results *[1 mark]*.

p.53 — Strong Acids and Weak Acids

Q1 Any one of, e.g. sulfuric acid / nitric acid / hydrochloric acid *[1 mark]*.

Q2 Change in pH = 3 − 6 = −3
Change in concentration of H^+ = $10^{-(-3)}$ = 10^3 = 1000
So, the concentration of H^+ is 1000 times greater at pH = 3 than at pH = 6 *[1 mark]*.

p.54 — Reactions of Acids

Q1 calcium carbonate + hydrochloric acid → calcium chloride + carbon dioxide + water *[1 mark for calcium chloride, 1 mark for carbon dioxide and water]*.

p.55 — The Reactivity Series

Q1 $2Na_{(s)}$ + $2H_2O_{(l)}$ → $2NaOH_{(aq)}$ + $H_{2(g)}$ *[1 mark for correct reactants and products, 1 mark for balancing, 1 mark for state symbols]*

p.56 — Separating Metals From Metal Oxides

Q1 $2ZnO + C → 2Zn + CO_2$ *[1 mark for the correct products, 1 mark for the correctly balanced equation]*

Q2 Carbon is less reactive than calcium and therefore will not reduce calcium oxide / Calcium is more reactive than carbon, so calcium oxide won't be reduced by carbon *[1 mark]*.

p.57 — Redox Reactions

Q1 a) $Zn_{(s)}$ + $Fe^{2+}_{(aq)}$ → $Zn^{2+}_{(aq)}$ + $Fe_{(s)}$ *[1 mark]*

b) $Zn_{(s)}$ is being oxidised *[1 mark]*. $Fe^{2+}_{(aq)}$ is being reduced *[1 mark]*.

p.58 — Electrolysis

Q1 a) chlorine gas/Cl_2 *[1 mark]*

b) sodium atoms/Na *[1 mark]*

p.59 — Electrolysis of Aqueous Solutions

Q1 anode: $2Cl^- → Cl_2$ + 2e⁻ *[1 mark]*
cathode: Cu^{2+} + 2e⁻ → Cu *[1 mark]*

p.61 — Exothermic and Endothermic Reactions

Q1 exothermic *[1 mark]*

p.62 — More Exothermic and Endothermic Reactions

Q1

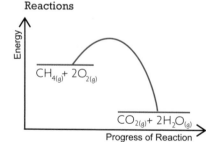

[1 mark for correct axes, 1 mark for correct energy levels of reactants and products, 1 mark for correct shape of curve linking the reactants to the products]

p.63 — Bond Energies

Q1 Energy required to break original bonds:
(1 × N≡N) + (3 × H–H)
= 941 kJ/mol + 1308 kJ/mol = 2249 kJ/mol
[1 mark]
Energy released by forming new bonds:
(6 × N–H)
= 2346 kJ/mol *[1 mark]*
Overall energy change:
= 2249 kJ/mol − 2346 kJ/mol = −97 kJ/mol
[1 mark]

p.64 — Cells and Batteries

Q1 Metal 2, Metal 3, Metal 1 *[1 mark]*. Zinc is less reactive than all 3 metals, so the most reactive metal will make the cell with the greatest voltage, since there will be the biggest difference in reactivity *[1 mark]*. So the order of reactivity is simply the order of the size of voltage *[1 mark]*.

p.65 — Fuel Cells

Q1 O_2 + 4H^+ + 4e⁻ → 2H_2O *[1 mark for correct reactants and products, 1 mark for balancing]*.

p.67 — Rates of Reaction

Q1 The activation energy for a reaction is the minimum amount of energy that particles need to react *[1 mark]*.

p.68 — Factors Affecting Rates of Reaction

Q1 a) B *[1 mark]*, because the powder has a higher surface area to volume ratio than the solid strip *[1 mark]*.

b) B *[1 mark]*, because the 4 mol/dm³ KOH solution is more concentrated than the 2 mol/dm³ solution *[1 mark]*.

p.69 — Measuring Rates of Reaction

Q1 a) Add Na_2CO_3 to a flask containing HCl *[1 mark]* and take readings of the mass of the flask at regular intervals *[1 mark]* using a mass balance *[1 mark]*. / Add Na_2CO_3 to a flask containing HCl *[1 mark]* and take regular readings of the volume of gas released *[1 mark]* using a gas syringe *[1 mark]*. **Maximum of 3 marks available.**

b) E.g. cm³/s *[1 mark]*

p.70 — Two Rates Experiments

Q1 E.g. volume of HCl added *[1 mark]*, mass of magnesium used *[1 mark]*.

p.71 — Finding Reaction Rates from Graphs

Q1 a) E.g.

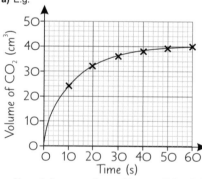

[1 mark for correctly marking on all 6 points, 1 mark for choosing a sensible scale for the axes, 1 mark for drawing a line of best fit.]

b) E.g.

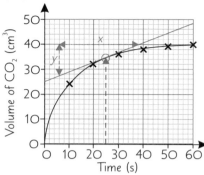

$y = 40 - 27 = 13$,
$x = 38 - 6 = 32$,
rate $= y \div x = 13 \div 32 = 0.4$ cm³/s
[1 mark for drawing a tangent at 25 s, 1 mark for correctly calculating a change in y from the tangent, 1 mark for correctly calculating a change in x from the tangent and 1 mark for a rate between 0.3 cm/s and 0.5 cm/s]

p.72 — Reversible Reactions
Q1 A system is at equilibrium when both the forward and reverse reactions are happening at the same rate *[1 mark]*.

p.73 — Le Chatelier's Principle
Q1 a) More $N_2O_{4(g)}$ produced *[1 mark]*.
b) No effect *[1 mark]*.
c) More CO_2 produced *[1 mark]*.

p.75 — Hydrocarbons
Q1 a) $C_{10}H_{22}$ is more viscous than C_5H_{12} *[1 mark]*.
b) $C_{10}H_{22}$ has a higher boiling point than C_5H_{12} *[1 mark]*.
c) $C_{10}H_{22}$ is less flammable than C_5H_{12} *[1 mark]*.
Q2 $C_3H_8 + 5O_2 \rightarrow 3CO_2 + 4H_2O$ *[1 mark for correct reactants and products, 1 mark for correctly balancing]*

p.76 — Fractional Distillation
Q1 It suggests that the hydrocarbons in petrol have a lower boiling point than those in diesel *[1 mark]*.
Q2 It's hot at the bottom and cooler at the top *[1 mark]*.

p.77 — Uses and Cracking of Crude Oil
Q1 Number of C atoms = 5 − 2 = 3
Number of H atoms = 12 − 4 = 8
Formula = C_3H_8 *[1 mark]*

p.78 — Alkenes
Q1 C_8H_{16} *[1 mark]*
Q2 Carbon monoxide *[1 mark]*, carbon *[1 mark]*.

p.79 — Reactions of Alkenes
Q1
```
    H  H  H
    |  |  |
H — C — C — C — H
    |  |  |
    H  H  H
```
[1 mark]
Q2 The solution turns from orange to colourless *[1 mark]*.

p.80 — Addition Polymers
Q1 A polymer is a large molecule formed when lots of monomers join together *[1 mark]*.
Q2
```
  ( CH3 H )
  (  |  | )
—(  C — C )—
  (  |  | )
  ( H  CH3)n
```
[1 mark]
```
  ( H  H )
  ( |  | )
—( C — C )—
  ( |  | )
  ( H  C2H5)n
```
[1 mark]

p.81 — Alcohols
Q1 $C_2H_5OH + 3O_2 \rightarrow 2CO_2 + 3H_2O$ *[1 mark for correct products and reactants, 1 mark for correctly balancing]*

p.82 — Carboxylic Acids
Q1 a) You would see bubbles of gas form *[1 mark]* as carbon dioxide is produced *[1 mark]*.
b) sodium carbonate + methanoic acid → sodium methanoate + water + carbon dioxide *[1 mark]*

p.83 — Condensation Polymers
Q1 E.g. water *[1 mark]*
Q2 one *[1 mark]*

p.84 — Naturally Occurring Polymers
Q1 polypeptides *[1 mark]*
Q2 E.g. proteins/polypeptides *[1 mark]*, starch/cellulose *[1 mark]*, DNA *[1 mark]*.

p.86 — Purity and Formulations
Q1 a) The sample melts over a range of temperatures *[1 mark]*. The melting point is lower than that of pure aspirin *[1 mark]*.
b) Any range or single value within the range: 141-200 °C *[1 mark]*

p.87 — Paper Chromatography
Q1 During paper chromatography, the molecules of each chemical in the sample move between the stationary phase and the mobile phase *[1 mark]*. The mobile phase moves through the stationary phase over the course of the experiment, and anything that's dissolved in it will move with it *[1 mark]*. The distance a compound moves through the stationary phase depends on how long it spends dissolved in the mobile phase compared to on the stationary phase *[1 mark]*. Since different compounds will interact differently with the mobile phase and the stationary phase, they'll move different amounts through the stationary phase, and so be separated from each other *[1 mark]*.

p.88 — Tests for Gases and Anions
Q1 Chloride *[1 mark]*

p.89 — Tests for Cations
Q1 The metal ions burn with a distinctive colour *[1 mark]*.
Q2 a) Al^{3+} *[1 mark]*
b) $Al^{3+} + 3OH^- \rightarrow Al(OH)_3$ *[1 mark]*

p.90 — Flame Emission Spectroscopy
Q1 Flame emission spectroscopy can be used to identify the metal ions in mixtures *[1 mark]*, whereas flame test can only be used for substances that contain a single metal ion *[1 mark]*.

p.91 — The Evolution of the Atmosphere
Q1 Sedimentary rocks are formed when organic matter such as plant deposits or the shells and skeletons dead of marine animals fall to the seabed *[1 mark]*. These become buried and compressed by sediments over millions of years forming rocks *[1 mark]*.

p.92 — Greenhouse Gases and Climate Change
Q1 Any three from, e.g. polar ice caps melting / sea levels rising / costal erosion / changing rainfall patterns / some regions may have too much or too little water / it may be difficult to produce food / there may be an increase in the frequency and severity of storms. / the distribution of wild species may be affected *[1 mark for each, up to a maximum of 3 marks]*.

p.93 — Carbon Footprints
Q1 E.g. governments can put a cap on the amount of greenhouse gases that a business can emit and issue licences for set amounts of emissions up to this point *[1 mark]*. They can also impose taxes on companies according to the amount of greenhouse gases that they emit to encourage them to cut down on emissions *[1 mark]*.

p.94 — Air Pollution
Q1 E.g. particulates (soot) *[1 mark]*, unburnt fuels *[1 mark]* and carbon monoxide *[1 mark]*.

p.96— Ceramics, Composites and Polymers
Q1 E.g. thermosetting polymers don't soften when heated whereas thermosoftening polymers do *[1 mark]*.

p.97 — Properties of Materials
Q1 $(14 \div 24) \times 100 = 58.33 \approx 58\%$ *[1 mark]*

p.98 — Corrosion
Q1 The pure iron nail will rust *[1 mark]*. E.g. the galvanised nail won't rust due to the zinc forming a protective layer *[1 mark]*.

p.99 — Finite and Renewable Resources
Q1 A finite resource, such as e.g. crude oil, will take a long time to replenish *[1 mark]*. On the other hand, a renewable resource, such as e.g. timber, can be replaced within a relatively short time scale *[1 mark]*.

p.100 — Reuse and Recycling
Q1 E.g. saves energy needed to extract metals from the earth / conserves limited supplies of metals from the earth / cuts down on the amount of waste going to landfill *[1 mark for each]*.

p.101 — Life Cycle Assessments
Q1 Choice of material / manufacturing and packaging / using the product / product disposal *[1 mark for each]*.

p.102 — Potable Water
Q1 E.g. filter the water first, using a wire mesh followed by sand and gravel beds *[1 mark]*. Then sterilise the filtered water using chlorine / ozone / UV radiation *[1 mark]*.

p.103 — Waste Water Treatment
Q1 Screening *[1 mark]*, sedimentation *[1 mark]*, digestion (aerobic / anaerobic) *[1 mark]*.

p.104 — The Haber Process
Q1 A temperature of 450 °C is used because this is high enough to ensure a fast rate of reaction without decreasing the yield of ammonia by too much *[1 mark]*. A pressure of 200 atm is used in order to maximise the rate and the yield of the reaction. Higher pressure would be too expensive *[1 mark]*. An iron catalyst is used in order to speed up the rate of reaction *[1 mark]*.

p.105 — NPK Fertilisers
Q1 E.g. potassium chloride / potassium sulphate *[1 mark]*

Index